Traces on the Appalachians

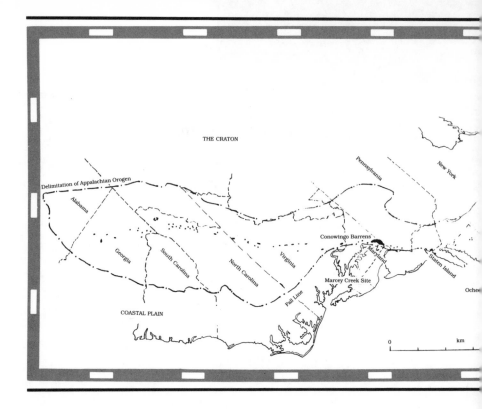

Traces on the

Kevin T. Dann

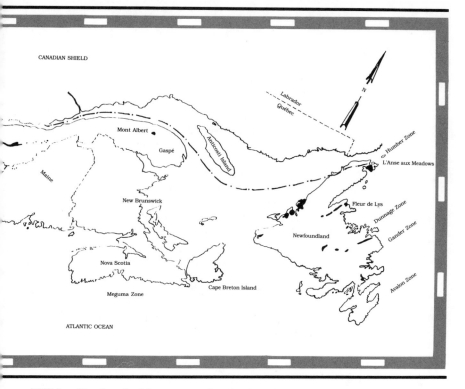

MAP 1   The Appalachian orogen showing location of major regions of serpentine and associated ultramafic rocks (black areas)

Appalachians

A Natural History of Serpentine in Eastern North America

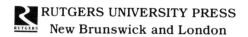

RUTGERS UNIVERSITY PRESS
New Brunswick and London

Figures 1, 2, 3, and 9 reproduced by permission of the Smithsonian Institution from "Stone Implements of the Potomac-Chesapeake Tidewater Province" by William Henry Holmes, plate numbers 35, 78, 102, and 67. In *Fifteenth Annual Report of the Bureau of American Ethnology*. Washington, D.C.: Smithsonian Institution, 1897.

Figure 5 © 1987 The Detroit Institute of Arts, reproduced by permission of The Detroit Institute of Arts, Founders Society Purchase, William H. Murphy Fund (Accession No. 39.559.43)

Quote on pages 19–20 reprinted by permission of the Library of the National Museum of American Art and the National Portrait Gallery

Quote on page 26 reprinted by permission of the Academy of Natural Sciences of Philadelphia

Quote on pages 88–89 reprinted by permission of the Vermont Historical Society

Quotes on pages 116–117 reprinted by permission of the New England Botanical Club, authority of the Council

For Joyce,
who has given me the freedom to pursue arcane paths,
and who continually renews me
when I return to her

Contents

List of Illustrations

Figures

Maps

Preface

My first encounter with serpentine came in 1977, as an undergraduate at the University of California at Santa Cruz. I was enrolled in the Natural History Field Quarter, a sort of roving naturalist's Chautauqua, which took a group of students all over California to marvel at and, it was hoped, begin to understand the incredible diversity of that landscape. As an adjunct to an exploration of the Big Sur coast, we headed inland to the Diablo Range section of the Los Padres National Forest. We had been told tales of an eerie, barren landscape there that harbored some rare plants—*Lavia discoidea*, a strange rayless tarweed; *Streptanthus insignis*, a lovely crucifer; and San Benito monardella (*Monardella benitensis*)—and where there was a curious array of native conifers. One of our leaders, Ray Collett, was the director of the University Arboretum and had, it seemed, ferreted out every bizarre conifer population in California. We knew he had a penchant for hybrid pines and other phytogeographic nightmares, but none of us knew that he'd been bitten by the serpentine bug, and that he was about to expose us to it.

After piloting our two vans along some precipitous logging roads, we ended up at what looked like the seventh ring of Dante's Inferno. Desolate gray-green hills broken only by an occasional sickly-looking digger pine stretched in every direction. All of us—geologists and botanists alike—were outraged that we'd left the paradisiacal Big Sur for this hell. We found little consolation in the words of William H. Brewer, who'd been there two hundred years earlier as the botanist for the Whitney Geological Survey of California. In 1861 he was witness to the same scene: "chain after chain of mountains, most barren and desolate. No words can describe one chain, at the foot of which we had passed on our way—gray and dry rocks or soil, furrowed by ancient streams into innumerable canyons, now perfectly dry, without a tree, scarcely a shrub or other vegetation—*none*, absolutely, could be seen. It was a scene of unmixed desolation, more terrible for a stranger to be lost in than even the snows and glaciers of the Alps."

At least when Brewer had been there, there had been some life. He and state geologist J. D. Whitney had spooked a herd of pronghorn on their arrival to the area, and that evening they took up residence at the hacienda of the superintendant of the New Idria quicksilver mine. It was quicksilver—mercury—not rare plants that brought the Whitney survey to New Idria. In 1861 the serpentine hills sported villages of miners, carpenters, masons, and blacksmiths; mule-drawn ore trains converged on the area from mines scattered throughout the barren hills; furnaces dotted the landscape, flanked by huge stacks of cordwood and marked by plumes of white smoke rising from the stacks. When we pitched our tents at New Idria, elongated ore dumps and conical tailings heaps were the principal features, along with the rotting timbers of the adit entrances and a few sheds. Pronghorn and mine workers were equidistant specters. New Idria was the quintessential California "ghost town."

By the time we left New Idria, we were thoroughly fascinated by the effect that the green rock had on the overlying vegetation. We saw a colony of Palmer oak (*Quercus dunni*), a shrubby oak whose main population was off on the edge of the Mojave Desert. We saw a swarm of hybrid pines intermediate between Coulter (*Pinus coulteri*) and Jeffrey (*P. jeffreyi*) pines. We saw creeks flanked only by pines and incense-cedar, and a single willow, named for William Brewer (*Salix breweri*). Along the creeks was also confined one of our most ubiquitous herbaceous companions on our California travels— blue-eyed grass (*Sisyrinchium bellum*). It disappeared, however, out on the shingly serpentine slopes. A little farther afield, on San Benito Mountain, we saw the San Benito evening primrose (*Camissonia benitensis*), which grows only there and in one other nearby location. At New Idria, California's most dramatic serpentine "barren" (the term usually used by scientists and laymen alike to describe such places), we were introduced to the "serpentine phenomenon"—range disjunction, endemism, but most of all, uniqueness. On later trips—to the Siskiyou Mountains of northern California, the Red Mountains of the Mount Hamilton Range, in the Sierra Nevada—we had other encounters with serpentine vegetation, each adding new data, as well as more questions, to our serpentine picture. While in New Zealand in 1978, I accidentally came upon one of the Southern Hemisphere's most spectacular serpentine barrens, at Dun Mountain on the South Island. Though composed of different taxa, the same bizarre plant patterns were represented there.

In 1979 I ended up in Rhode Island, working at a wildlife refuge run by the Audubon Society of Rhode Island. There were no serpentine endemics in the state, but occasionally I would hear stories about an ancient soapstone quarry, and I knew soapstone was geologically "related" to serpentine. I eventually found my way to the aboriginal quarry, which by that time was merely a pockmarked outcrop of rock pinned between a supermarket parking lot and a highway exit ramp. This became one more ultramafic landscape to file away in my memory. My curiosity was still growing.

When I moved to Vermont in 1981, I began asking botanists if they were aware of any serpentine barrens in Vermont. I'd noticed on a geological map of the state that there were ultramafic rocks running the length of the state and was sure there had to be some interesting flora associated with them. Aside from a dunite outcrop near the summit of Haystack Mountain, no one knew of any unique vegetation on ultramafic rock in Vermont. I'd aroused the curiosity of one of the state's finest plant hunters—Peter Zika—who, with geological maps in hand, began visiting outcrops of dunite and serpentine. Rare plants began to turn up. In Vermont, we found not the spectacular serpentine barrens of New Idria, nor even the high degree of endemism of the other California "ultramafites" (ultramafic rock), but a more subtle, understated effect. In Vermont's northern, glaciated, mesic clime, the "serpentine syndrome" (as A. R. Kruckeberg has called the array of effects that ultramafic rock has on overlying vegetation) was an entirely different scientific problem.

The soapstone-serpentine connection was still lingering in my mind and grew stronger as I botanized sites that had deposits of soapstone associated with them. When I talked to archaeologists, they all assumed that the many pieces of soapstone that had been encountered from habitation sites around the state had their source in southern New England. With so many native sources close at hand, I couldn't help but feel Vermont had its share of aboriginal quarries. Had nineteenth-century quarrying obliterated all traces of earlier activity? I began poking around old soapstone quarries, looking for the bowl-shaped depressions I'd first seen at the Ochee Springs quarry in Rhode Island. I was curious as to why the two rock types—serpentine and steatite (soapstone)—were associated with each other in some places and not in others. I began reading the geological reports rather than just using the maps to find the outcrops. I sat in on an Appalachian geology course and was introduced to the concept of ophiolites, and I realized there was another story in the archipelago of ultramafic deposits along the Appalachian mountains, a story not told by the state geological reports that I'd been perusing from the

1950s and 1960s. Plate tectonics had rewritten that geological story, and it began to call me as strongly as the botanical and archaeological ones.

Now I was going into the field (and library) with three lines of inquiry and felt that each was interesting enough that nonscientists would also be interested in them. *Traces on the Appalachians* is my attempt at telling that story. Though it draws on the particular narratives that three sciences have to tell regarding ultramafic rock, the book relates a broader tale. It is in essence a natural history of a type of rock. A natural history of an organism is a treatise on "who, what, when, and where" via a description that serves both the scientist and the layperson. *Traces on the Appalachians* is classic natural history, then, in that it outlines what serpentine (and the geologically related steatite) is, how it formed, and where it is found. It serves the layperson by summarizing in nontechnical terms a vast body of scientific information. For the scientist familiar with one or all of the unique aspects of serpentine, the book serves as an informal history of a small subset of nineteenth- and twentieth-century American science and also establishes a connection between three independent disciplines to one of their objects of inquiry.

Just as natural histories of whales and woodpeckers and worms have changed dramatically as naturalists of each generation have brought their own insights and questions to bear on earth's myriad life forms, so have geologists shifted their views of serpentine and its kindred rocks—steatite, dunite, and others. In the two centuries that Americans have been practicing science, archaeologists have likewise come to know more and different details of the human use of soapstone, and botanists have learned new facts about the interaction of serpentine soils and the flora associated with them.

The question remains: *why* tell the story of this particular rock? It is a question often asked of the scientist by the nonscientist. Why study coral reefs? Why study spruce trees? Why study rattlesnakes? Why study serpentine? If you are persistent and keep peeling away the logical answers—"it is important economically"; "it will make the world a better place"; "it will satisfy my curiosity"—you are often left with a surprising, illogical core of motivation: "because it is beautiful." I love serpentine, love to find it outcropping green and glistening from its surrounding sea of schist. I love to hold a piece of soapstone in my hands, to etch it with my fingernails or sand it smooth. I love how endlessly varied its colors and textures and shapes are, and how it merges with the plant community above it to form something uniquely appealing to the eye. So, at its barest level, *Traces on the Appalachians,* and the sorts of science it describes, is an aesthetic endeavor. If the lay reader comes away yearning to carve a soapstone pot, hungry to see a serpentine landscape, or anxious to begin a rock collection; if a scientist or two discovers that there is more than just his or her story to tell about the green rock, then this book will have made its mark.

Though many people helped me to define and refine this story, three in particular stand out. Dan Gade of the Department of Geography at the University of Vermont encouraged me to pursue what was an unorthodox approach to geographic research. Bill Howland of Middlebury College's Northern Studies Program provided critical editorial help as well as lively discussion about many of the topics that have ended up in the book. Peter Zika, who is as fine a naturalist as anyone I know, tirelessly and generously answered botanical questions and was a cheerful, whimsical, and knowledgeable companion in the field.

Traces on the Appalachians

or'i gin, n. [Fr. *origine*; L. *origo, originem*,
from *oriri*, to rise]
1. a coming into existence: beginning
2. that in which something has its
beginning; root; cause

or' o gen, n. [from Gr. *oros*, mountain,
genes, origin]
1. belt of deformed rocks (e.g., the
Appalachian orogen)

o rog'e ny, n.
1. the process of forming mountains

Introduction

Words have lives of their own, and as a scientific term, the word *serpentine* **has had a sinuous and variegated life history. Some** of that history will be discussed later, but it's necessary at the outset to justify and explain it as the subject of this book. In its narrowest sense, serpentine applies only to the serpentine group of minerals—antigorite and chrysotile—which have the general chemical formula $Mg_3Si_2O_5(OH)_4$. There are certain rocks that are predominantly composed of these minerals, and so it is natural that these would come to be called serpentine as well. (Today, geologists more frequently call these rocks "serpentinites.") The one fact the reader may remember from high school geology is that there are three major categories into which geologists divide all rocks—sedimentary, igneous, and metamorphic. Serpentine rocks are metamorphic, having originated as the igneous rock peridotite, which is composed largely of two minerals—olivine and pyroxene. More will be said of this later.

The reader will find that in this book, serpentine is used interchangeably with other terms—*ultramafic*, for example. Ultramafic implies that a rock contains more than 70 percent ferromagnesian (iron- and magnesium-containing) minerals. Ultramafic rocks appear in many places on the earth, in many different configurations. There are layered ultramafic "suites" (different rocks often found in association with one another), such as the Great Dyke in Africa. Bisecting Zimbabwe along a north-south line of some 500 kilometers, these ultramafic rocks carry some of the world's greatest deposits of chrome and asbestos, and above them grows an impoverished grassland or sometimes shrub savanna differing markedly from the woodland on adjacent granitic rocks. There are the kimberlites and carbonatites, volcanic intrusions associated with fault zones all over the world and famous for being important sources of diamonds. There are ultramafic lava flows in Canada, Western Australia, and South Africa. In any classification of ultramafic rocks, however, one type is clearly distinguished from all others—alpine-type peridotite and serpentinite associations, of which the vast majority of ultramafic rock in the Appalachians are an example. The geological background of these deposits will be discussed in the chapter titled "Freestone and Footwarmers."

In the alpine-type ultramafic suite (also known as an "ophiolite"), the border of the rock mass is often steatite, which is a massive, impure, talc-rich rock. At all of the locations discussed in the book, there are greater or lesser deposits of steatite associated with serpentine. This geographic consideration is what justifies their consideration together in *Traces on the Appalachians.* They are not the same rock, nor are they *always* found in association, but they trace their geologic origins to a similar source, and they have each in their own way presented scientific mysteries.

If ophiolites, and thus serpentine, are found all over the world, why is the book limited to the Appalachian Mountains? This great mountain chain does not hold the most spectacular ophiolites for the geologist; it does not have the most anomalous plant communities for the botanist; its steatite quarries, both historic and prehistoric, are small and mostly inactive. But the Appalachians were the mountains on which American scientists first tried their ideas. Long before J. D. Whitney and William Brewer would ever look on the New Idria barrens, generations of American scientists around Washington, Philadelphia, New York, and Boston posed many questions about the ultramafic rocks of the Appalachians. The scientific theories that were applied to the serpentine rocks of western North America were rooted in the Appalachians, just as surely as Appalachian geology was rooted in European intellectual traditions. A more direct answer to "Why the Appalachians?" is that the Appalachians are my home. They are the landscapes that are most familiar and friendly to me. The New Jersey–New York highlands, a bit west of the nearest ultramafic deposits, are where I first wandered into the Appalachian forest, where I first stumbled upon abandoned farms and old quarries, and where I first wondered why the rock there was different from the red sandstone of my backyard. These are the same elements that led me along the serpentine path.

Traces on the Appalachians is intended as *a* story, not *the* story of serpentine. It brings together for the layperson three stories centered around one region—the Appalachians. For the botanist, geologist, and archaeologist, there is no new information here. Botanists interested in serpentine vegetation may turn to R. R. Brooks's recent work *Serpentine and Its Vegetation: A Multidisciplinary Approach,* a 450-page review of the world's ultramafic flora. Geologists interested in ophiolites have R. G. Coleman's 1977 work, *Ophiolites,* and the collection of papers edited by P. J. Wyllie, *Ultramafic and Related Rocks,* not to mention the dozens of papers that appear in journals each month reporting on recent research regarding ophiolites. Archaeologists curious about prehistoric steatite use would do better to look at issues of *Archaeometry* or recent books, such as P. J. Ericson and B. Purdy's *Prehistoric Quarries and Lithic Production,* than here. *Traces on the Appalachians* unites the three disciplines via a historical view of scientific inquiry; therein lies its utility. A theme that emerges is that scientific theories are nothing if they are not stories. They explain and clarify for the moment what was previously obscure, but like stories, they are subject to change, revision, or outright rejection. The reader should consider this book a story. It is full of science and history, but it is in essence a narrative, a serpentine narrative about a green rock.

Asaxusas

Some April perhaps five thousand years ago, a band of men and women—ancestors of the tribes that in historic time came to be called the Susquehannock, Nanticoke, and Delaware—set out from their oyster-gathering place on Chesapeake Bay up the strong waters of the Susquehanna, the "great island river." At the fall line, where the crystalline Piedmont rocks dive fault-bound beneath the Coastal Plain, the band portaged their dugouts around the dangerous rapids. They continued upstream to one of the islands near the mouth of the Conowingo, where they set up camp. The shad run that had brought the band to this place ended before too long, but there were pike, perch, and bass to be caught as well. It was probably June or July, when Juneberries, huckleberries, and wild currants were plentiful, that one of these prehistoric canoe-wanderers left his nets to gather wild fruits and hunt deer. He may have followed the Conowingo north toward its headwaters, or perhaps he pulled his dugout ashore on the west bank of the great island river, then set out. Perhaps it was while retrieving a spear that had missed its mark, or while looking for the sunny, cliffy spots where the blueberries ripened earliest, that this canoe-wanderer came across a strange, soft rock. Surely this stone could not serve as spearpoint or knife, but perhaps it would do for an atlatl weight or some other purpose, and so the prehistoric prospector placed the soft rock in his tool kit. When he returned to camp, he showed the strange rock to the others. Perhaps he had already fashioned an atlatl prototype, or a net sinker, or a small gorget for one of his children, when one of the women asked him to bring back more of the soft stone. Using one of the sharp stone blades usually used for skinning shad, she sat fashioning a small bowl out of the soft rock. Scattered about the fire ring of the campsite, among the drying racks of fish, was her cookware—skin bags and bark buckets that could not go over the fire but had to receive heated stones.

After she finished shaping the crude bowl, she placed water and a few pieces of perch in it and set it over the fire. Before long the meal inside the bowl hissed and sputtered, yet the bowl remained intact. She went to pick it up, but there were no handles; she must remember this next time. She showed it to the other women and offered to them the meal from inside the bowl. Tasting the warm food, they realized at once the possibilities for this new material. The soft rock was "soapstone," or as the Greeks called it, steatite. *Stear* is the Greek word for fat or tallow, and the rock of both Mount Olympus and the and the lower Susquehanna have the same greasy feeling. We have no inkling of what these prehistoric canoe-wanderers, or their prehistoric contemporaries, called the rock. During the ethnographic present, the Karok Indians of the Klamath River region called it "asaxusas," literally "soft rock."

Our grandparents knew soapstone in the form of foot warmers, boot dryers, griddles, and stoves. We may have used a soapstone sink in chemistry lab in high school, or perhaps we've seen the slick ads for soapstone stoves in *Country Journal, Solar Age,* or one of the other "new age" magazines. Although the uses have changed, the properties that make soapstone useful have always remained the same, and the silent, insightful invention of that woman on the great island river has been repeated over and over.

The properties? Steatite is actually a massive, impure variety of talc, a mineral whose chemical formula is $Mg_3Si_4O_{10}(OH_2)$, or hydrous magnesium silicate. Talc has a three-layer sheetlike crystal structure—two silica tetrahedral layers enclose an octahedral layer in which all octahedral positions are filled with magnesium ions. Talc crystallizes in monoclinic systems, usually as foliated, radiating, compact masses or, rarely, as tabular crystals. It is white, greenish, bluish, or brownish, with white streaks; it is transluscent to transparent; it has a pearly luster in large sheets; and it feels greasy. Cleavage is perfect in one direction, and fracture irregular. The hardness is only 1 and specific gravity is 2.58−2.83. Soapstone (talc) also has a high index of latent heat retention.

What this means to a nonmineralogist is: talc and soapstone are chemically neutral (negative hydroxyl ions on the tetrahedral layer are neutralized by the positive magnesium ions on the octahedral layer), thus making it a good material for chem lab sinks; the perfect one-directional cleavage means it is an excellent lubricant, since the layers slip easily past each other; and talc is one of the softest minerals. The designation "1" refers to the Mohs hardness scale, which very simply tests relative resistance to scratching. A fingernail (2.5) scratches soapstone but cannot scratch a copper coin (3.5). (The hardest mineral, a diamond, at 10, scratches all other minerals and cannot itself be scratched.) Being so soft, soapstone has naturally always been carved.

The high index of latent heat retention is why the Vikings quarried huge blocks of steatite to set in front of their bonfires—at night, after the fire died, the quarried soapstone block radiated the heat it had absorbed. This property is what makes it better than cast iron for wood stoves, and it's what made the woman's experiment back in the shadows of prehistory a successful one. She'd "discovered" the perfect cookware.

Whether ten thousand years ago or yesterday, ideas spread, and others of that prehistoric tribe shared in the new knowledge. Perhaps the following year half a dozen men left the great island river to retrieve the few loose blocks of soft stone that lay near that first spot. After they exhausted the loose stone they began to work at the bedrock itself, beginning at the places where it outcropped in the stream beds and the hillsides. For over two thousand years they came to this and other spots, eventually developing a whole set of stone tools with which to quarry the material—chisels, scrapers, abraders, shavers, drills, reamers, gouges, and even crude stone hoes for exposing the material. It may be that the quarry outings became as regular as the trips to the shad-run islands, since the bowls would often break or even wear out under continued use. They continued until about 1200 B.C., about the time when two innovations, agriculture and pottery, reached this part of the Eastern Woodlands. In coastal southern California, in the area where the Canaliño, Gabrieliño, and Chumash lived, the twin innovations never appeared, and the trips to the soapstone quarries continued into historic times, until the people, or at least their culture, which made the trips necessary, had been eradicated by the Europeans.

Archaeologists would refer to the band as people of the "Susquehanna Archaic" tradition, deduced from the repeated findings of a similar artifact complex (steatite bowls, Susquehanna "broadspear" points, and atlatl weights) throughout the area around Upper Chesapeake Bay and the lower Susquehanna. Soapstone bowls are so diagnostic of the late (or more correctly, "Terminal") Archaic, that many archaeologists refer to the period as the "Transitional," for it was indeed transitional from the diverse seasonal hunting-fishing-gathering lifeway of the Archaic, to the sedentary, agricultural way of the Woodland period, which started around 1000 B.C. The cultural and technological changes reflected by the archaeological record for this period are dramatic, and among the most radical innovations was the displacement of bulky soapstone bowls by cooking and storage vessels made of local clays.

The Susquehanna Archaic people were not alone in their use of steatite, and whether by independent invention or through cultural diffusion, a whole array of their Archaic contemporaries were quarrying soapstone and fashioning it into bowls. From the Lauderdale phase in Alabama through the Stallings Island–Susquehanna tradition in the Piedmont of Georgia and the Carolinas, north to the Potomac, then beyond the Susquehanna to the Orient complex centered on Long Island Sound, steatite bowls were a cultural common denominator. Looking back into prehistory through the window of archaeology, all along the Appalachian orogen, steatite chronologically precedes pottery. In the soil of Stallings Island, Georgia, and Jamesport, Long Island, alike, shards of steatite stop where pottery shards begin. In the Southeast, the first pottery is a thick, coarse ware, with grass or rootlet fibers mixed with the clay to strengthen the pottery, and before long the steatite quarry locations faded from the collective cultural memory. But around the lower Susquehanna, the Potomac, and the Delaware, the memory lingered; the first pottery (Marcey Creek ware to the archaeologists) was made with crushed steatite as temper.

The Marcey Creek site (*see Map 2*) is located at the head of Tidewater, overlooking the Little Falls of the Potomac, which demarcate the fall line here more drastically than the slowly migrating rapids on the lower Susquehanna. This site is on the right bank of the Potomac and covers less than a quarter of an acre near the crest of a precipitous hill, about 170 feet above river level. During prehistoric

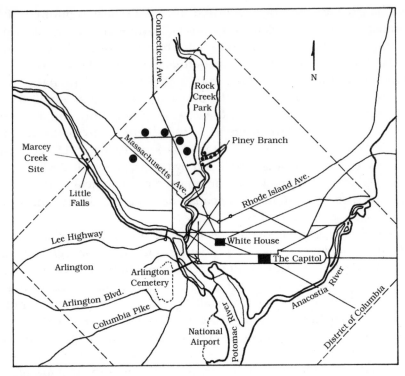

● soapstone quarry
• quartzite quarry

MAP 2   Washington, D.C., area archaeological sites. (After Humphrey and Chambers, 1977)

times, water could be drawn from a small spring, now dry, which flowed into Marcey Creek, about 100 yards from where the stream cascades over a falls into the Potomac.

When William Henry Holmes of the U.S. National Museum explored the Potomac River Valley in 1890, he studied and described most of the major village sites and cultures to be found in the area known as "Tidewater." Although situated so perfectly at the head of Tidewater, the Marcey Creek site was not reported by Holmes. It was not until 1948 that Carl Manson excavated and described the site. Manson noted that the lower levels of the Marcey Creek site produced lugged steatite containers (the handles that that first pot maker had forgotten, had, by Marcey Creek time, become standard equipment), accompanied by large spearpoints of the Savannah River–Susquehanna—Orient "fishtail" types. In the brown sandy soil above this as-semblage were found similar but smaller points, a perforated winged "bannerstone" (atlatl weight), a fully grooved axe, a steatite "net sinker," and steatite-tempered pottery. These first ceramics were flat-bottomed, straight-edged, lugged containers virtually identical in shape to the stone vessels from the soil below. Thus the soil at the Marcey Creek site revealed the link between the stone bowls of the preceramic Archaic period and the early ceramics of the Woodland period.

In 1890, when Holmes was doing his survey of Tidewater Poto-mac, there were no concepts of "Archaic" or "Woodland" periods. The waters of American prehistory were still quite murky, with many anthropologists trying to fit the archaeological evidence of man in the New World into a classification parallel to that of western Eu-rope. Museum cases in New York, Boston, Washington, and other American cities were filled with rudely chipped stones labeled "Ameri-can Paleolithic Implements." Because of their crude shape, Ameri-can scientists (most notably Charles C. Abbott and George F. Wright) assigned these implements an antiquity of between ten and twenty thousand years.

Holmes's training was as an artist, not an anthropologist, and in fact, it was in pursuit of art that Holmes came to Washington in 1871. At art school Holmes met Mary Henry, daughter of Joseph Henry, first secretary of the Smithsonian Institution. (Henry was a physicist known for his work on the electromagnet—a "henry" is an electrical unit named for him.) He and his family lived in "the Castle," the eccentric red sandstone building that stands at the center of the Mall, and it was here that Henry collected everything from weather reports to Indian baskets.

Holmes visited Mary Henry at the Smithsonian, and it was on his first visit here that, while sketching a bird, he came to the attention of one of the many naturalists then loosely associated with the Smith-sonian. He soon came to be employed to draw fossils for the paleon-tologist Fielding B. Meek and mollusk shells for the zoologist William H. Dall. This led to Holmes's appointment as artist on Ferdinand Hayden's U.S. Geological Survey of the Territories. For six years Holmes stayed with Hayden as artist and geologist, exploring the mountains of central Colorado, the Yellowstone region, and the San Juan Valley in New Mexico and Arizona. It was among the ruins of the mysterious cliff dwellers of the San Juan Valley that Holmes became fascinated with some of the fundamental questions of North American archaeology.

When Holmes turned his attention to the problem of "Paleolithic" man in America by his examination of the Piney Branch site, no teams of archaeologists were available, and so he trained his own and personally oversaw their work. (In "Random Records of a Lifetime," Holmes's unpublished autobiography, he admits to having employed Ahab's gold dubloon trick, promising a dollar for each artifact recovered intact. In this manner, he discouraged reckless excavation, which would have yielded little useful information.) Because of his association at the Bureau of American Ethnology with some of the finest anthropological minds of the day—John Wesley Powell and Lewis H. Morgan, for example—Holmes's methods and field techniques were exemplary, and further, his geological training from the Hayden Survey years enabled him to make important geomorphological, ecological, and cultural observations on the region. Finally, the trained eye of the artist Holmes led him to make detailed examinations of artifacts to determine the process of manufacture.

At the Piney Branch site on Rock Creek in Washington, Holmes discovered an "ocean of paleoliths"—crudely percussion-flaked quartzite boulders. Stimulated perhaps by his observation of Southwest Indians making and using tools, Holmes undertook the replication of the "paleoliths," showing them to be the rejected remains and by-products of the process of creating stone projectile points, knives, and other tools. (He calculated that there were usually twenty failures for each successful tool.) In "Stone Implements of the Potomac-Chesapeake Tidewater Province," in the *Fifteenth Annual Report of the Bureau of American Ethnology*, Holmes's theory regarding the tool-making process is convincingly supported by his detailed, step-by-step illustrations.

The massive leather-bound, exquisitely illustrated volume that is the *Fifteenth Annual Report of the Bureau of American Ethnology* (BAE) is a government publication and today finds itself in the same "Government Depository Libraries" that house such mundane items as census reports, *Statistical Abstracts of the United States*, and the *Congressional Record*. In 1897, when it was published, one could have purchased a copy for five dollars. Today, the report seems priceless, for to flip through the yellowing, tattered pages, to stop at the tissue-paper-protected lithographs and the gold leaf on the title page, to hold its weight in one's hands, is to be transported back to the nineteenth century.

The volume contains photographs of Holmes and his "archaeological" laborers, leaning against their shovels and pickaxes at the Piney Branch site, dressed in tails and top hat. There are photographs of the steatite quarries at Connecticut Avenue (*see Figure 1*), which Holmes and his men excavated simultaneously with the Piney Branch site, the shapes of incipient stone bowls clearly visible in the bedrock, looking as if the aboriginal quarrymen had just left their work to go home for supper. There are the sketch maps of the quarries, their exact location precisely marked with an "X" between the contour lines along Connecticut Avenue. (Today, no sign of the quarries can be found, the Bureau of Standards building standing where for thousands of years men and women came to gather the soft rock.) And there are Holmes's pen-and-ink drawings of his own hands replicating the tool-making process, showing not only objects he himself had made, but also the analogous forms from the rejected piles of quartzite boulders at Piney Branch.

Although the first half of the *Fifteenth Annual Report*, a description of the Piney Branch site and Holmes's refutation of the American "Paleolithic" theory, established Holmes's reputation as a careful yet inventive scientist, the second half, a description of the Washington-area steatite quarries, is equally important. A series of scale drawings illustrates the steps in the steatite-shaping process, from the ovoid mass cut from the quarry to the rough finished vessel (*see Figure 2*). Drawings of quartzite quarry picks, with the ghostly outline of the original boulder shown in dotted lines, make the connection for the reader between the tool workshops at Piney Branch and their eventual use in shaping the steatite bowls. Photos of quarry shop rejects show the marks from these picks with perfect clarity.

The two sections of this report might have remained as two isolated bits of scientific evidence, but Holmes did not miss the chance for some well-founded inductive reasoning. He asked the question, "Are [the steatite quarries and the quartzite boulder quarries of the District of Columbia] . . . all probably of one age and the work of one people, or are they separated by long periods of time and marked differences in art characters?" Holmes could not help but think that these two spots, situated in the same valley and less than a mile and a half apart, would have been visited by the same prehistoric peoples. The old "paleolith" adherents thought otherwise, their

FIGURE 1   William Henry Holmes in an excavation at the Connecticut Avenue
steatite quarries

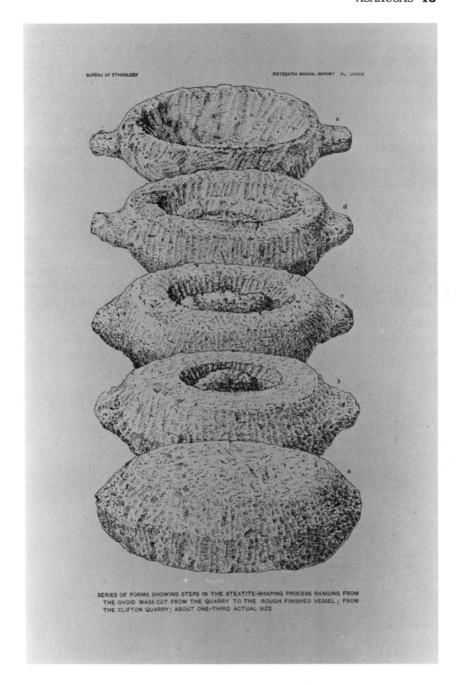

SERIES OF FORMS SHOWING STEPS IN THE STEATITE-SHAPING PROCESS RANGING FROM THE OVOID MASS CUT FROM THE QUARRY TO THE ROUGH FINISHED VESSEL ; FROM THE CLIFTON QUARRY; ABOUT ONE-THIRD ACTUAL SIZE

FIGURE 2   W. H. Holmes illustration of steps in the steatite bowl-shaping process

geomorphically poor stratigraphic vision seeing one quarry type (steatite) with little depth (5–6 feet at most) and less overburden, while the boulder quarries could be measured in tens of feet both in depth and overburden of new surficial material. Holmes's more finely tuned stratigraphic eyes saw the two quarries as existing under very different geomorphic conditions—the steatite pits, excavated in solid rock on the crests of hills, where there was little or no material available to cover the site save the leaves from the trees, and the cobble quarries, situated on the slopes of the hills directly beneath the loosely compacted Tertiary and Quaternary sands and gravels of the Coastal Plain. Holmes found synchronicity here, and though his conjecture as to the actual age of the sites eventually proved wrong, he had grasped that the two groups of "quarrymen" were one and the same people. Holmes's work showed that they'd followed Rock Creek and Piney Branch in pursuit of their prehistoric needs to both the cobble piles and the outcrops of "asaxusas," as time kept pushing toward that cursed/blessed day when prehistory yielded to history.

Holmes's Hope

It is fitting that W. H. Holmes had an opportunity to give artistic expression to the synchronicity that he had perceived at the Piney Branch and Connecticut Avenue quarries, and if one knows where to look and looks closely enough, it can still be seen today at the National Museum in Washington. Across the Mall from the building where Holmes was first drawn into the world of science is the National Museum of Natural History—twenty acres of artifacts of the natural world. If one can pull oneself away from the new, brightly colored multimedia exhibits on tribes of the Amazon Basin or the mechanisms of evolution and descend to the ground floor, one can find it. Tucked away in one of the wings of the now drab Hall of North American Indians is a life-size diorama showing a group of aborigines at work at the Piney Branch quarry, surrounded by the refuse of their tool making that became Holmes's "ocean of paleoliths" (*see Figure 3*). This, and a number of other dioramas in the hall, was designed and implemented by Holmes, whose "life group" approach to museum display was a sharp break from the endless shelves of sterile artifacts typical of Victorian-era museums.

At the foot of the plaster aborigines in Holmes's Piney Branch diorama lie some of the original artifacts collected at the boulder quarry; the neat five- and six-digit catalog numbers are plainly visible on many of them. There among the cobbles sits a single roughed-out steatite bowl, looking slightly out of place, but making for us the link to this other prehistoric industry. For some reason, perhaps simply because space would not allow, there is no diorama of the Connecticut Avenue soapstone quarries. Instead, next to the Piney Branch diorama is a life group depicting aboriginal steatite quarrying at "Pots Valley" on Santa Catalina Island, off the southern California coast.

For perhaps five thousand years, the ancient "Canaliño," Gabrieliño, and Chumash had paddled their big dugouts across

FIGURE 3   Piney Branch Indian village diorama designed by W. H. Holmes

the Santa Barbara Channel to the island, and when Holmes visited in the fall of 1898, he found that a few square miles of the soapstone ridge had been worked over. Three thousand years ago the people from the coast had hunted seals and whales in those big dugouts, and burned the oil from these marine mammals in steatite lamps carved from the rock of Santa Catalina Island. They also left behind small effigies in soapstone of killer whales, which in late winter prowled the waters off the island's shores, looking for newborn elephant seal pups.

Just across the hall from the Pots Valley and Piney Branch dioramas is a door that leads to the heart of the National Museum, one of the storage areas where the "stuff" of over a century of collecting is kept. There, on a tall metal shelf unit, are the unfinished bowls from the Connecticut Avenue and other D.C.-area steatite quarries. On faded labels in quill pen are the names of the collectors: Frank Hamilton Cushing, Lewis Kengla, W. H. Gill, and Holmes.

The tools of the steatite quarry are there too. The huge grooved celts and axes on these shelves and the smaller quartzite quarry picks filed away in drawers speak of their use through their worn edges and the traces of talc that still cover them. Many of the tools and steatite pot fragments look familiar, since they were the models for Holmes's illustrations in the *Fifteenth Annual Report of the BAE*. There is some strange comfort felt here; although the quarries are covered by government buildings and housing developments; the record of prehistoric technology is preserved in these cluttered aisles. One can also feel a great sense of loss, that the people who developed this technology and practiced it over a few millennia have vanished, and that our most dedicated efforts to preserve the relics of a past culture are diminished in the face of our complete annihilation of its historic descendants.

William Henry Holmes was concerned about "preservation," and there in the National Museum are housed some thoughts and words on this subject by the same man who helped to fill the building with artifacts and exhibits. In the National Anthropological Archives are over 4,000 cubic feet of records and manuscripts—correspondence, ethnographic and archaeological field notes, sketches, transcripts of oral history, and other materials from such a diverse array of American anthropological figures as John Wesley Powell, Jesse Walter Fewkes, Franz Boas, Robert F. Heizer, James Mooney, and Otis T. Mason.

Among the Holmes papers is his "Random Records of a Lifetime," which includes a letter from Holmes to Colonel Clarence Shirrell, director of the Rock Creek and Potomac Commission, regarding the preservation of the Piney Branch quarries. Holmes, age seventy-nine, was then serving as director of the National Gallery of Art. On April 29, 1925, Holmes wrote:

> my recent visit with you to Piney Branch has aroused anew the hope that this secluded little valley may yet be rescued, at least in large part, from the ruthless invasion of suburban improvement. This valley, as you know, deserves the city's attention not only on account of its romantic beauty and desirability as a park area, but especially for the reason that it bears on its forest-covered slopes one of the most important historical sites east of the Allegheny Mountains, the site on which for hundreds, possibly thousands of years the Indian tribes of the Potomac Valley quarried quartzite boulders from which they roughed out their implements of war and the chase. The numerous tribal groups dwelt in villages scattered along the banks of the Potomac and its tributaries unmolested. They fished in the beautiful streams and hunted in the primeval forests. They had

not the forebodings of the fate that awaited them—the complete surrender to foreign and merciless invaders of the birthright of their race. The first white man appeared in 1620 and the last Indian disappeared from the valley in 1690. Since that date barely ten generations have passed, yet today the only permanent mark of their presence here, the only existing reminder that such a people ever dwelt within the District of Columbia, are these deposits of quarry shop refuse covering acres of ground on the site which will in a few years be the very center of the Capital city of the usurping race. A most serious question thus presents itself to our people—shall we go on selling and buying and selling again the hills and valleys of their birthright, amassing fortunes upon fortunes, without a thought of their former existence or their sacrifice? In the world's history, races have succeeded races in possession of the garden spots of the world, and are we to follow the example of the barbarians of the past? Are we the barbarians of the present?

Strange Plantscape
on the Octoraro

**A few miles down the Susquehanna from the shad-run islands
at the mouth of the Conowingo lies Octoraro Creek. To the Susquehannock, "Octoraro" meant "the place where money and many
presents are given."** But to the Susquehannock, the creek itself
had many names, and "Octoraro" may have only referred to a single
ford or rapids along its meandering course. To the native peoples of
this continent linear features such as streams were seen as points
on a continuum. For the Susquehannock, there were probably a
dozen other names—for example, "place where wild currants grow,"
"at the rapids"—that defined the stretch of water we call the Octoraro. River, ridge, or island, a few centuries of collective cultural
place-naming gave breath to the perception of any linear landscape
feature as a series of specific places. Linear place-names to us are
truly linear; we encompass the length of mountain ranges and great
rivers equally, having seen them stretched out flat on maps since
sixth-grade geography.

Perhaps the place where money and many presents were given
was the broad, flat place on the west bank of the big bend just below
Lee's Bridge. Called "Horseshoe Ford" or simply "the Oxbow" by
some, it is a place where today the corn grows tall on soil that is renewed by seasonal inundations of rich silt from the Octoraro. Here
the echoes of hammers that pounded at Wood's Chrome Mine a century ago spill out of the patch of second-growth woods that splits the
big floodplain cornfield into two.

Standing in that place today, you can look across the Octoraro to
a ridge that supports a strange pattern of vegetation. As your eyes
move to the right, surveying the ridge, the canopy changes from tall
red and scarlet oaks, tulip trees and hickories, to a stunted scraggly
canopy of scrub and pitch pine, blackjack and post oak. Move closer
and there's one feature in particular that catches the eye, a bald spot

where the ridge steepens above the Octoraro. Perhaps this spot caught the eye of some canoe-wanderer fifty centuries ago when the meander lay a few inches this way.

The soil on the bald spot can barely be called soil; it is more like rubble, and there is a lot of drab green rock exposed. Most of the plants growing on these olive outcrops are, locally, strangers. They are generally absent from the nearby woods. There are the harebell, *Campanula rotundifolia;* the northern bedstraw, *Galium boreale;* and the wild lettuce, *Lactuca canadensis.* The northern affinity of the latter two is suggested by their specific epithets. The most conspicuous plant here is not one of these northerners though; it is the mouse-ear chickweed, which grows in wide mats on the rocky slope. The mouse-ear chickweed is extra hairy here, and locally one would be hard put to find this particular plant anywhere else, for as F. W. Pennell wrote, it "has an occurrence probably as restricted as that of any plant in eastern North America."

The olive rock is serpentine, and the cliffs at the Horseshoe Bend below Lee's Bridge expose the same rock that extends for some 35 miles, from Little Elk Creek in Chester County, Pennsylvania, west-southwestward to the Susquehanna and beyond into Harford County, Maryland. Variations of the plantscape here on the Octoraro stretch with the drab green rock in both directions (*see Map 3*).

This part of the Piedmont is still farm country; corn, wheat, and hay define the landscape. Two hundred years ago it was even more so, and to the generations of farmers that have worked the land here, the plantscape of the serpentine has always been known as "the barrens," since it would never support farming. On the serpentine soils, corn is knee-high in September as well as July. In some places richer soils have been deposited over the serpentine (as at the inner bend of the Oxbow), but on the "honeycomb-rock" serpentine soils, no amount of lime or potash will help, and crops stay just as stunted as the pitch pines and blackjack oaks that grew there centuries before. Nor is the land much good for pasturage or timber, and so the barrens have remained relatively untouched by humans.

The key to the infertility of serpentine soils lies in their chemistry. Actually a group of minerals, the serpentines (antigorite, lizardite, and chrysotile) are closely related to talc, being hydrous magnesium silicates with the formula $Mg_3Si_2O_5(OH)_4$. Unlike talc, which has a relatively simple structure, serpentine is structurally and chemically complex. One gets the sense of this complexity in the field; the habit

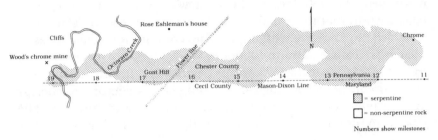

MAP 3   The State Line barrens

and color of the rock changes dramatically from place to place. Some generalizations that are important to both the farmer and botanist regarding serpentine can be made. Iron and magnesium content is high, and so usually are the nickel, chromium, and cobalt concentrations. At the same time, serpentine is low in calcium, nitrogen, potassium, phosphorus, and molybdenum.

A farmer faced with making serpentine soils productive would have plenty of reason to despair. Anyone who has ever bought fertilizer could see why. The three numbers at the top of the fertilizer bag refer to the N-P-K content (nitrogen, phosphorus, and potassium), all of which are in short supply in soils derived from serpentine. Calcium, which is of importance in tissue production, is also very low in concentration. Finally, chromium, cobalt, and nickel are elements that might be added to the soil of a plant you want to kill, and these are relatively abundant in serpentine soils.

The physical properties of serpentine soils are not too favorable either, the soils being mostly shallow and stony. Here's where the riddle of serpentine infertility gets sticky. Coarseness and shallowness of soils cause poor root penetration and greater drought susceptibility. This reduces the number and types of plants that can grow on serpentine. Often, the scanty vegetative cover exacerbates the drought problem, since the plants are more exposed to excessive wind and insolation. With fewer herbaceous plants and trees, and thus less humus production, the soil develops slowly and is more easily eroded. Soil erosion typically leaves a shallow stony soil, supporting few plants, which in turn tends to perpetuate stony shallow soils. From such biological Gordian knots was the science of ecology born, and plant ecologists the world over have long been fascinated by the riddles of serpentine vegetation.

The first North American plant ecologists were, of course, those native people now hidden in the shadows of prehistory, and it is almost certain that those canoe-wanderers from the great island river observed the "barrens." Although "plant community" *sensu* Gleason, Clements, Tansley, Braun-Blanquet, and Whittaker meant nothing to that hunter near the Conowingo headwaters, his mental map was undoubtedly phytosociological, grasping both structure, phenology, and floristics of his surrounding community. Floristics and phenology, to him, meant to look for huckleberries in June and cattails in August.

In the barrens, one cannot help but notice plant structure. That proto-Susquehannock hunter had to pay attention to structure, since the dense growths of briar could thwart any foot-bound hunter's movement. But the browse is poor on the barrens, and the rabbit hunting was always better than the deer hunting. The bare spots and lowered canopies—structure—were probably embedded in the cultural memory as the "places of briar and cottontails."

In fact, prehistory is nearly all conjecture, and so one must look at the written word to know with certainty what thoughts serpentine vegetation has stirred. In the sixteenth century, the Italian botanist Caesalpino described a plant restricted to the *sassi neri* (black stones) of the Upper Tiber Valley. *Sassi neri* is still the Tuscan term for serpentine rocks, and Caesalpino's "Lunaria quarta alias Alysson," now known as *Alyssum bertolonii*, is still abundant in that area.

It was not until the mid-eighteenth century that a botanist described the vegetation of the "Nottingham" barrens (so-called because they lie principally in the township of West Nottingham in Chester County; they are also known as the "State Line," "Conowingo," or "Goat Hill" barrens). That botanist was a Quaker farmer named John Bartram, whom Linnaeus called "the greatest natural botanist in the world." It was en route from Philadelphia to the Carolinas in 1760 that Bartram visited the barrens.

Taxonomic Tangles

Philadelphia was still a colony in 1760, and just as the colonies lacked independence from the mother country, so in many ways did scientific minds of the New World lack independence from the scientific ruling class of Europe. While the Royal Society of London heatedly debated whether or not swallows hibernate under water, American naturalists only timidly put forth more credible scientific ideas. Principal among these naturalists were a group of Philadelphia Quakers, including Benjamin Franklin and John Bartram, who together established a scientific academy to be composed of a few "ingenious and curious men" who would devote themselves to a "study of naturall secrets arts and syences." Thus in 1744 was the American Philosophical Society born, giving impetus to Philadelphia's place as the center of North American natural history studies and publications for the following century.

John Bartram begat William "Billy" Bartram, and these two Bartrams begat much of the American scientific inquiry of the late eighteenth and early nineteenth centuries. The American Philosophical Society became the Academy of Natural Sciences of Philadelphia in 1812, and around these two institutions were centered the collecting activities of the Bartrams, André Michaux, Henry Muhlenberg, Humphrey Marshall, Benjamin Smith Barton, Frederick Pursh, William Darlington, C. S. Rafinesque, Thomas Nuttall, and William P. C. Barton.

The Nottingham barrens are just 35 miles from Philadelphia, and other smaller serpentine barren outliers are even closer. It was thus natural that they came to be visited by these prominent early American botanists. The entire barrens community caught the eye and held the attention of these early botanists, but the component parts, the plants, needed description. To describe a culture, you collect potsherds and projectile points; to describe a plant species you collect plants, lots of them, and this is what these early botanists did. Many of these plant collections were destined to find their final resting place in the Academy of Natural Sciences building in Philadelphia. In that herbarium one can become uncommonly familiar with the botanists of the barrens. There among the over 1,250 collectors and 2 million specimens are serpentine barrens plants collected by William Baldwin, Pursh, Darlington, Rafinesque, J. W. Harshberger, Bayard Long, F. W. Pennell, and E. T. Wherry. Here are the quarry of the many plant hunters, each herbarium sheet preserving the place and date of capture, as well as other information.

If one goes to aisle 6 of the "Local" section of the academy herbarium and opens the big red compressor to locate the Portulacaceae, snug between the Aizoaceae and the Caryophyllaceae, one can find the genus *Talinum* with the single species *Talinum teretifolium* Pursh, the fameflower, in a folder on the compressor shelf. The fameflower is restricted to serpentine sites in southeastern Pennsylvania, though farther south it is found on other xeric soils, especially sand. Fameflower may be seen on the barrens in June, but one must go at midday, when the sun is high, for only then do the bright purple flowers open, and they close by late afternoon. William Darlington of West Chester was especially taken with this little plant, and attached to a specimen he collected from the Nottingham barrens is a letter to C. W. Short, the retiring botanist who succeeded Rafinesque at Transylvania University in Lexington, Kentucky. The letter, dated March 7, 1832, reads: "I have collected some roots of the *Talinum teretifolium* [which] I herewith send you. They are very hardy. If you will, plant them in pots or boxes. I have no doubt they will nearly all grow and flower during the summer and that you may have a chance to examine the plant. It grows naturally on serpentine rock, indeed I have never found it elsewhere, and always where that rock comes to the surface. I will be glad to hear how you succeed with it towards fall. Yours truly, William Darlington, West Chester."

This type of exchange flourished among the early American botanists, leading not only to a growth in botanical knowledge, but also to a great deal of taxonomic confusion. The first published descriptions of many plants were often written by botanists who had never seen the plants in the field. Those who did have extensive field knowledge of a particular plant in their own area were at a disadvantage when it came to describing a wide-ranging species. In an era of travel by horseback, few botanists could speak confidently of the differences in morphology and phenology of a species found from New York to Alabama. A herbarium specimen allows only a freeze-frame look at an individual plant whose morphology changes, more or less, throughout the growing season. A plant that is pubescent with ovate leaves today may be glabrate and lanceolate a week from now. For this reason, the herbarium specimens that were examined from distant parts often left an incomplete picture.

Such was the case with the mouse-ear chickweed, *Cerastium arvense* L., and the herbarium sheets at the academy, as elsewhere, preserve the record of both the initial taxonomic confusion and its ultimate resolution by a more recent curator, Francis W. Pennell. *Cerastium arvense* is a large flowered species of mouse-ear chickweed that was originally described from Europe by Linnaeus. As people have become more cosmopolitan, so has *Cerastium arvense*, and its range is now known to extend throughout the North Temperate zone of Asia and North America and into the South Temperate zone. This expansion is due both to anthropogenic dispersal and to our increased knowledge of the geographic distribution of the plant.

In the eastern United States, widespread on sandy or sterile soils, and especially on rocky cliffs, is a *Cerastium* with linear or narrowly lanceolate leaf blades, which Frederick Pursh in 1814 aptly named *Cerastium tenuifolium* Pursh. The wider-leaved hairier plant of Pennsylvania serpentine Pursh incorrectly took to be Linnaeus's *Cerastium arvense*.

In New York, John Torrey had given the name *Cerastium oblongifolium* Torrey to plants that D. B. Douglass had collected from the shores of Lake Erie and Chester Dewey sent from western Massachusetts, neither of which came from serpentine. Henry Muhlenberg had also gotten into the act, describing in his 1813 catalog a specimen sent to him by William Baldwin from "the Barrens, Chester County" as *Cerastium villosum* Muhlenberg, "*new species.*" The only problem was that Rafinesque had described the same plant in 1808 from "Newcastle County, Delaware, and Chester County, Penn."

When William Darlington published his *Flore Cestrica* (quaintly subtitled "An Herborizing Companion for the Young Botanists of Chester County, State of Pennsylvania") in 1837, he noted that Dr. Torrey believed the hairy plant of the Pennsylvania serpentine not to be *Cerastium oblongifolium*, and so he adopted Muhlenberg's *Cerastium villosum*. Also, there in the academy herbarium is preserved a specimen from West Chester, gathered by Darlington in

May 1831, which bears a note saying that Dr. Torrey "thinks it may be a non-descript." Obviously, Darlington was not sure what to think of the whole *Cerastium* business.

After the young University of Pennsylvania student F. W. Pennell had spent the summers of 1908 and 1909 "visiting by carriage, bicycle, and train nearly all the Serpentine Barrens in Delaware and Chester counties," he also was not quite sure what to think. In his report "Flora of the Conowingo Barrens of Southeastern Pennsylvania," published in 1910 as volume 62 of the *Proceedings of the Academy of Natural Sciences of Philadelphia*, Pennell lists simply *Cerastium oblongifolium* Torr., although he comments on the confusion.

In all of young Pennell's ramblings—to the Middletown barrens, Sugartown barrens, Serpentine Ridge, Cedar barrens, West Chester, Sconneltown, or "Strode's Mill," Brinton's Quarry, Unionville, and the Nottingham barrens—he had never come across the cliffs on the Horseshoe Bend of the Octoraro, where the "extra hairy" *Cerastium* could be found. Pennell, aided by the automobile, did not visit the cliffs of the Octoraro until 1920, but he visited them each year thereafter until 1930, when he reconsidered the *Cerastium* confusion in a paper entitled "On Some Critical Species of the Serpentine Barrens." With all the perspicacity of twentieth-century botanical hindsight, it may be seen that Pennell categorically set the *Cerastium* record straight. Pursh's *Cerastium tenuifolium* was renamed by Pennell *Cerastium arvense;* Rafinesque's *C. velutinum* and Muhlenberg and Darlington's *C. villosum* became *C. arvense* variety *villosum* (*villosum,* meaning hairy); and the silky, broad-leaved plant that grows on mats on those cliffs of the Octoraro became *C. arvense* variety *villosissimum* (literally, "extra hairy"). The type specimen (F. W. Pennell #10767), collected in fruit on September 21, 1920, lies in the herbarium of the Academy of Natural Sciences of Philadelphia. It is the type specimen of a very rare plant, one that is included in the Federal Register of the Department of the Interior as an "endangered species."

The Serpentine Gestalt

The Nottingham barrens are themselves endangered, as are all the barrens. When Pennell toured the serpentine "islands" in the summers of 1908 and 1909, they were essentially undisturbed. Traditionally perceived as waste places, useless for agriculture or sylviculture, they had escaped the ax and plow. But the twentieth-century population boom and new postindustrial wealth turned land into "real estate," and real estate operators found that even the barrens could be bought up cheaply to be turned into house lots. With a few truckloads of topsoil, they could easily replace the barren broomsedge patches with a real lawn. Today, on some of these lawns can be seen gnarled pitch pines, red cedar, or stunted post oaks; these are not ordinary suburban landscape plantings, but telltale relics of the serpentine flora once present there. These barrens are thought to be the most complete and diverse example of serpentine ecology in the eastern United States, yet they have been reduced from an area of about 2,000 acres to roughly half that.

Near the edge of the Nottingham barrens, not far from Goat Hill, are some of the serpentine house lots. If one crosses the road and follows the power line right-of-way, it is possible to avoid the greenbriar tangles that can make foot travel in the barrens a misery. The landscape there is wild and desolate; the pygmy pitch pine forest is broken by many shingly serpentine openings. Fifty inches of rain fall here annually, but it looks for all the world like a semidesert.

The visitor to the barrens is struck by the overwhelming desolation of the place. Maybe it is the pile of serpentine rubble with the makeshift wooden cross and the coyote skull mounted on it that gives one this feeling of desolation. Perhaps it's the depauperateness of the vegetation, each plant looking a bit undernourished. Maybe it's the rubble heaps from the old magnesite mines, or the turkey vultures that circle overhead and nest in the old mine entrances.

The bits of iron tools and pieces of pottery strewn about on the drab green rock-soil suggest that the barrens have always been perceived this way; they seem to say that a hundred years ago it was as acceptable to despoil the barrens as it is today.

There is a gripping Gestalt about this landscape—it is beautiful and ugly at the same time. It has the same appearance as the serpentine barrens at New Idria, in San Benito County, California, where the only trees that grow are three pines—Jeffrey, Coulter, and Digger—and the little incense cedar *Calocedrus decurrens.* Otherwise, the area is all chaparral and bare spots. Motorcycles run rampant there (even though there are signs that warn the cyclists that the dust their bikes kick up contains dangerously high levels of asbestos), and the land is useless enough to have a microwave tower on one of the craggy serpentine summits. The cinnabar in those hills that the Yokut Indians used for red pigment yielded quicksilver (mercury) to the Anglos, who used the magic liquid-metal to amalgamate the precious silver and gold. The turkey vultures are there too, but the adits lead after the elusive mercury instead of magnesite.

Dun Mountain on the South Island of New Zealand has the same Gestalt. The luxuriant southern beech (*Nothofagus*) forest on the adjoining sedimentary rocks stops dead at the dunite mountain, where trees yield to shrubs and boulder-strewn openings harbor a depauperate-looking endemic herbaceous flora. Turkey vultures never reached this distant Pacific island. There is the harrier instead, the accipiter-turned-vulture, soaring low over the barrens in search of carrion.

That Gestalt that haunts the barrens visitor at New Idria, Dun Mountain, the "Tôte Alps" (dead Alps) of Europe, the Keen of Hamar on Unst in the Shetland Islands, Mount Apoi in Japan, or Mont Albert on the Gaspé Peninsula is formed by some very definable characteristics of the serpentine vegetation. The most notable is the relative openness of the plant cover. The pitch pines, blackjack oaks, and dwarf chinquapin oaks that make up the barrens "forest" near Goat Hill don't really form a forest at all. It is more a parkland, or savannah, the trees spaced widely with patches of broomsedge and other grasses between. A mile away, on soils derived from nonserpentine rock, one can stand in a mature woodland and look around to see a rich, dense forest; red, white, and scarlet oaks, mockernut and shagbark hickories, basswood and tulip trees, sweet birch and other trees grow tall over flowering dogwood, sourwood, witch hazel, and redbud. The ground below this vegetative profusion is equally rich; May apple, jack-in-the-pulpit, true and false Solomon's seal, windflower, and spring ephemerals soak up the little light that gets through. It's cool and moist there, on a day when in that pine-oak-broomsedge savannah all is thirsty.

There is not only an opening of the forest canopy on serpentine, but also a *lowering.* Many of the trees that grow on serpentine are dwarfed compared to their stature on nonserpentine soils. Perhaps it is the scale of the serpentine vegetation that both attracts and repels the observer; it is a scale more fit to human size, less humbling than the neighboring mesophytic forest. No cathedrals would have been inspired by this scrawny wood.

The opening and lowering of the canopy could be seen as a strand in another one of those ecological Gordian knots that serpentine produces. Where the sun penetrates the canopy, soil moisture and the humidity at the shrub and herb levels are reduced drastically, creating a good niche for shade-intolerant, xerophytic species. Seven thousand years ago, the Hypsithermal brought the leathery-leaved oaks and their xeric associates to the Pennsylvania Piedmont and left many stranded here on the barrens when the climate changed to a cooler, moister regime than during the more xeric Hypsithermal.

The Hypsithermal brought grasses of the high plains and left here at Goat Hill and other barrens the broomsedges or bluestems, *Andropogon* spp., *Panicum annulum*, and the tufted hairgrass, *Deschampsia caespitosa*. It brought other grasses that are now less widespread off the prairie—two of them, the northern dropseed, *Sporobulus heterolepis*, and tall grama grass, *Bouteloua curtipendula*, grow here at Goat Hill. Poor competitors in more favorable settings, the prairie disjuncts hang on here where no mesophytic plants can oust them.

The nongraminoid herbs of serpentine sites are equally characteristic of dry open habitats; to see many of them one would have to visit the Pine Barrens or some droughty granitic outcrop in the Piedmont farther south. On the bare areas, where the motorcyclists like to go, there is *Arabis lyrata*, the lyre-leaved rock cress, a frail-looking plant made frailer by the fact that its tufted leaves often die early in the season and disappear. There is the slender knotweed, *Polygonum tenue*, that seems to grow in the very worst places on the barrens. Pennell's hairy mouse-ear chickweed, *Cerastium arvense villosum*, is there, as is Darlington's fameflower, *Talinum teretifolium*. There is the depauperate aster, *Aster depauperatus*, which Darlington, in his *Flore Cestrica*, called the *Aster miser*, the "miserable or starved aster" of sterile places. The taxonomists now call the little aster of the barrens distinct from those of other infertile places, and one can call *Aster depauperatus* a true serpentine "endemic."

On the Nottingham barrens the prostrate mountain pink, *Phlox subulata*, is not particularly conspicuous; patches of it appear as at home in the oak-andropogon parklands as out on the treeless barrens. But on other barrens in the Pennsylvania-Maryland Piedmont, it is spectacular, in late April turning some serpentine hills into a sheet of flame. There are "Pink Hills" at the Tyler Arboretum in Lima, Pennsylvania, the Unionville barrens, and elsewhere.

Particularly abundant on the open barrens is *Arenaria stricta*, the little erect sandwort. The Latin *arenaria* means "of sand," yet the genus *Arenaria* is almost equally characteristic of serpentine. There are *A. humifusa*, *A. groenlandica*, and *A. rubella* of the magnesian gravels of the North American Arctic and sub-Arctic. The large-leaved Arenaria, *A. macrophylla*, makes its way south on serpentine rock from Labrador to the Shickshocks and then on the dunite deposits of Vermont all the way to Massachusetts. There on the Berkshire Hills of the New England upland, on a serpentine cliff (in Florida, the town just south of the west entrance to the Hoosac Tunnel) is found what is probably the southernmost population of *A. macrophylla*, growing with a *Cerastium arvense* that approaches the villose variety of the Nottingham barrens. The marcescent sandwort, *Arenaria marcescens*, conspicuous on the barrens at Mont Albert in the Gaspé, trails south across the Canadian border onto a north-facing dunite ledge near the summit of Haystack Mountain in northern Vermont. To these "serpentinophiles" there are no political boundaries, only the geologic boundaries laid down millions of years ago, but constantly changing with the ebb and flow of ice ages and orogenies.

Lines and Holes

**If you follow the power line that traverses the Nottingham bar-
rens south, dropping down to the valley of Pine Run, and then**
climb to the other side, you come to the area known as "Goat Hill."
The origin of this place-name is obscure, but it seems likely that it
derives from the fact that some farmer tried to make use of this land
once, pasturing goats among the clumps of broomsedge and hairgrass. At the top of the hill, near one of the big transmission towers,
lies the boundary between Pennsylvania and Maryland. There is no
marker here along the right-of-way, and one is hard put to know
which way the boundary would run, a compass needle being confused by the magnetic field that jumps from the 345-kilovolt lines up
above. It's the same magnetic field that buzzes in the ear and makes
the head of a visitor ache, and would have made some of the goats of
Goat Hill abort.

Though there's no sign of the state line in the open right-of-way,
you can walk east a few hundred yards through the pitch pines to
one of the little grassy openings so characteristic of the barrens and
see the ruins of the stone mound that was erected by Charles Mason
and Jeremiah Dixon in 1765. No monument lies here, though the
sixteenth and seventeenth milestones of the Mason-Dixon Line lie a
half mile east and west, respectively. On each milestone, a 7-foot-
high block of oolitic limestone, is the letter *P* facing north and the
letter *M* facing south, and every fifth mile are the "crown" stones,
with the coat of arms of the original two possessors engraved on
each side.

The "two possessors" were Lord Baltimore and William Penn,
whose land feud is one of the most celebrated on the continent.
While the English, French, Dutch, and Spanish warred and arbi-
trated for pieces of the New World, Charles I had granted a large

piece of that turf to Lord Baltimore in 1663. About the same time, the Quaker Penn had become interested in colonization of the land west of the Delaware and north of Susquehanna Fort, and petitioned for a tract of land lying north of Maryland. This was granted to him in 1681, and Penn and Lord Baltimore were left to work out "a true division and separation of the said provinces of Maryland and Pennsylvania.

It wasn't until two generations later that the two families got down to defining the line, and in 1760 they hired the young English surveyors Mason and Dixon to carry out the work. One wonders what the two men made of the barrens—they probably rejoiced that there was less tree-felling to be done along this section of the line, and that they could sleep comfortably here on Goat Hill, the "savages" that would hinder their progress farther west having already been driven out of these parts by colonists.

Mason and Dixon's line was finally ratified in the winter of 1769, but the proprietors collected taxes for only a few more years before the American Revolution wrested their princely domains from them. The next two centuries would see the drawing of new lines, for new uses. Around 1810 chromite, the ore of chromium, was discovered in the Bare Hills, an area of serpentine barrens near Baltimore. Most of the Bare Hills were part of a large estate belonging to Isaac Tyson, Jr., who saw that his treeless ridges might at last be worth something. By 1817 Tyson had begun looking for the other chromite deposits in the barrens of the state line area.

There is a story that says that Tyson was in the Bel Air Market in Baltimore one day in 1827, when he saw a cart containing some vinegar barrels held in place by mottled serpentine stones. The black mottling of the stones was chromite, and Tyson traced the stones to the "Glades" on the Reed farm in Jarretsville. The high-grade chromite was abundant there, and the Reed mine became so profitable that Tyson abandoned the Bare Hills. Tracing the chromite north via the barrens, Tyson eventually located the deposit on the inner side of the Horseshoe Bend in the Octoraro, and there the Wood Mine was born.

Before it closed, the Wood Mine reached a depth of 720 feet, and the mouth of the main shaft measured sixty feet wide and 90 feet long. William Glenn, the last superintendant at the Wood Mine, described the work there in 1880:

The power for pumping and hoisting is taken from the Octoraro Creek, which is 180 fathoms from the engine shaft. For hoisting, power is obtained from a 60 in. turbine, under 10½ ft. fall and transferred by a 6 in. hawser cable to proper machinery at the mine. For power for pumps, a wooden breastwheel 16 ft. high by 18 ft. long, is used 10½ ft. fall. The motion is transferred by 6″ × 8″ wooden flat rod 180 fathoms to the engine shaft. There are two Cornish plunger lifts in the mine, with 10 in. columns. . . . The mine makes from 60 gals. to 110 gals. per minute—depending on the season. For Business reasons, but a small force of men has been employed of late years. There is no reason to think they will not continue, as heretofore, to produce 500 tons to 600 tons yearly.

A 60-inch turbine, 16-foot-tall breastwheels, Cornish plunger lifts, men heading down into the mine shaft, the rumble of the carts as they drove over Lee's Bridge over the Octoraro, headed for Isaac Tyson's processing plant . . . "There is no reason to think they will not continue . . . to produce 500 to 600 tons yearly." The mine closed in 1891. Today the mouth of the main shaft is a little cattail-fringed frog pond, and in summer the barn swallows fly over from the big cornfield to skim the pond for a drink. The sound and fury are now dissipated.

Window on the Appalachians

Report C4 (1883) of the Second Geological Survey of Pennsylvania describes the magnesite and chromite mines of Goat Hill and environs. Although it was published under the direction of J. P. Lesley, this report on the geology of Chester County draws mainly from the work of Henry Darwin Rogers, the first state geologist of Pennsylvania. The bulk of the Rogers material is from *The Final Report of the State Geologist, 1858*, although the field observations that provide the foundation for his monumental volume were made by Rogers in the first six years of the survey, 1836–42. The state geological surveys were somewhat tenuous institutions in the mid-1800s, scoffed at by the rough-and-ready mining industry and ignored by the general public, and though the Pennsylvania State Legislature had intended to fund the survey for at least ten years, it ended its appropriation after only six years. J. P. Lesley, director of the second survey, looking back on this in 1876, wrote: "The language of science was then an unknown tongue, and sounded in the ears of the people like the chattering of animals or idiots. The disputes of geologists respecting doubtful points, if listened to at all, were regarded as good evidence of the worthlessness of their theories; and the truths in which they agreed seemed to clergy and laity alike the insanities of an exalted imagination, or the impious utterances of an irreligious temper."

Though it saw the premature demise of the first Pennsylvania Survey, 1842 was a milestone year in the history of American geology, for that year, in Albany, Henry D. Rogers and his brother William Barton Rogers addressed the recently formed Association of American Geologists and Naturalists. While Henry had been at work in the Ridge and Valley Province of Pennsylvania, William was visiting outcrops of the southern extensions of the province's folded and faulted Paleozoic strata in Virginia. Together, in 1842, they were prepared to comment "On the Physical Structure of the Appalachian Chain, as Exemplifying the Laws Which Have Regulated the Elevation of Great Mountain Chains Generally."

The key had really come to Henry that first summer of the newly born survey, when an assistant, John F. Frazer, had been making a survey along Yellow Creek in Huntingdon County. There, in one of the few lines of continuous one-dip section, straight across the "Old Age System" (Paleozoic strata), was represented a thickness of about 25,000 feet of sediments, from the Broad Top Coal Measures (Mississippian) at Hopewell to the Lower Silurian limestones in Morrison's Cove. Lesley later wrote: "From that moment everything went smoothly; all contradictions vanished; their back notes became luminous, and the northern outcrops of [James] Hall and [Lardner] Vanuxem, in New York, were seen to be all represented in the same regular order, although by an immensely enlarged scale, by the southern outcrops of the same formations in Pennsylvania." The Yellow Creek area provided the quantum leap in understanding that guided Rogers and the survey's work through its initial years and up to the address of 1842.

The first part of the Rogers brothers' address clearly described the folded mountains of the Ridge and Valley Province. They illustrated the marked asymmetry of the folds and the common occurrence of overturned strata, which show Mine Ridge and Hawk Mountain to be opposite limbs of the same great earth warp. They pointed out that the degree of asymmetry and overturning decreased as one progressed northwestward and they grasped the vision of a true Appalachian "system," distinguished by the great length and remarkable parallelism of fold axes and fault traces throughout the Appalachian chain. They perceived the close relation of the province's numerous thrust faults to major anticlinal axes, and their experience in both the northern and southern parts of the Ridge and Valley allowed them to contrast Henry's domain—the perfectly folded middle Appalachians—with that of William's highly faulted southern Appalachians. It was this address that established the Ridge and Valley of the middle and southern Appalachians as the "type" folded mountain belt; similar ranges elsewhere are today still considered to be "Appalachian" in structure.

After this descriptive leap forward, the Rogers brothers, in their explanation of the Appalachian structure, took a terrific backward fall. They rejected the idea in vogue at the time that vertical forces caused the disturbed strata, believing that such a regular system of folds could not have been formed by local vertical uplift of each fold. Tangential force alone also seemed an inadequate explanation, in that it did not account for one of the salient features of the folded Appalachians—the extraordinary parallelism of the folds. Instead, they proposed a model that embraced both systems of forces—vertical and tangential.

Though uniformitarianism was gaining a foothold by the mid-1800s, catastrophic notions died hard, and it was a catastrophe of awesome proportions that Henry and William envisioned as the cause of the Ridge and Valley folds. To the southeast, near the centers of curvature of the arching fold mountains, the Rogers brothers saw huge volcanic explosions that shook the deep sedimentary cover as if it were a blanket being shaken at one edge. The folds of this blanket were frozen into place as the lava underneath cooled and solidified, according to Henry and William Rogers.

While the chronology of the elegant structures of the mostly unmetamorphosed Paleozoic strata of the Ridge and Valley Appalachians was easily determined, not so the crystalline Appalachians that lay to the southeast. The once-sedimentary rock that made up the Blue Ridge, the Piedmont, and the New England Upland farther north was a complete bewilderment to William and Henry Rogers and their contemporaries; so highly deformed was this rock that much of it was assigned to the "Azoic," that dark realm that was thought to be "without life" due to the absence of visible fossils.

Then came the "Eozoic." The "Eozoic" dawn that made up the latter part of Archaean time to the nineteenth-century geologic soothsayers intimated life only in the graphite and limestone traces that threaded through the schists of the crystalline Appalachians. And in a great effort to further divide time (an expanse of time of which they had only an inkling), the Eozoic unfolded to reveal the "Laurentian" below, and the "Huronian," stepping-stone to the Paleozoic, above it.

Whether called Laurentian, Huronian, Archaean, or Eozoic, the crystalline rocks were indeed a puzzle, but Henry Rogers worked heroically at solving it. He looked hard at the contorted, metamorphosed schists, gneisses, and quartzites of Chester County and saw a "Primal" formation, composed of "upper slates," the "middle white sandstone," "lower slates or talc-micaschists," and "micaceous gneiss" and "coarse mica schist."

He took the elusive rocks and fit them into a theory of parallel overturned anticlinal folds and synclinal troughs, as if they would somehow yield their secrets as completely as did the unmetamorphosed rocks of the Ridge and Valley to the west. But thirty years after Rogers had made his observations, and after others had stared equally hard, J. P. Lesley could only say that "after an apparently copious and precise array of facts the geology of the whole district remains as confused and obscure as ever. The section along the Schuylkill is the key to the lock; but the key will not turn in the lock; the door remains closed." No Yellow Creek was to be found for the confounded crystalline rocks.

In Chester County, the crystalline formations were riddled with the strange green serpentine rock, and Henry Rogers detailed their relations as he saw them. His narrative runs through the outcrops of Unionville, Sugartown, Sconneltown, Strode's Mill, Blackhorse Tavern, Marshallton, and Brinton's Quarry—locations familiar to Darlington, Pennell, and the other barrens botanists. In the "township geology" tradition of the nineteenth-century state surveys, we learn the width of the outcrop near the old smithy on John Gheen's farm, the strike of the exposure near the Barren Hill schoolhouse, the dip of the rock in the vicinity of Maris's gristmill. The observations of strike and dip of outcrops were to Rogers and his science as important as the noting of the stratigraphy of artifacts to Holmes and his science, or the collection of herbarium specimens by Darlington to the science of botany. These methods are as fundamental to the three sciences today as they were one hundred years ago.

The locations of the serpentine and the description of their attitude stand today; the geological interpretations of the serpentine do not. Colored by the notions of the times, they seem as quaint as the Rogers brothers' volcanic blanket-shaking episode seems outlandish. In the Chester County report, the ideas are those of Rogers, Lesley, and Persifor Frazer. They represent what the prevailing thoughts were about the strange green rock at the time.

Rogers believed the "unstratified" serpentine areas to be igneous bodies, and the "stratified" serpentine (actually the chlorite and talc/soapstone "shells" surrounding the serpentine) to be schists that had been impregnated with an "infusion of magnesia" from the serpentine intrusion. Rogers was convinced of the distinction between "stratified" and "unstratified" deposits, though it seemed less impressive to his colleagues in Pennsylvania. Lesley was more concerned with the relations between serpentine and certain dolomitic limestones along the southern edge of the South Valley Hill, and farther east along the Delaware River in Northampton County. Lesley felt that the serpentine was a modified dolomite, which indeed was true of the spot on the Delaware; but Lesley had wandered too far in his musings, out of the eugeosynclinal realm, to the miogeocline, the "foreland" of a geologic idea that still lay a century away.

But in the Chester County report, it was Persifor Frazer who had the last word about the whole business. After pondering the relations of the limestone belt, the mica schists, the "syenitic granite," the "hornblendic gneiss," the "black rocks" (gabbro), and the serpentine, he concludes that: "The serpentine under no circumstances has any direct connection with a series of hypozoic or paleozoic strata of primary origin. It is clearly secondary whether metamorphic or (as is prevalent with some of the best European geologists) igneous."

Time and Rust

Frazer was probably referring to Alexandre Brongniart, the French geologist and mineralogist, who preferred the Euro-pean designation for the enigmatic green rock—"ophiolite." Brongniart and his contemporaries used ophiolite to describe a variety of serpentinized ultramafic rocks. "Ophiolite" or "serpentine," the rock had its etymological roots firmly planted in images of snakes. In 1897 a German mineralogist, Carl Hintze, published his *Handbook of Mineralogy,* in which he stated that the term *serpentine* had its roots in ancient Greece, where Dioscorides called it λίθος ὀφίτης and Pliny called it "ophite" (A.D. 77). Both terms have *ophis,* the Greek word for serpent, in mind, but just why this term was used is unclear. Some suggest that ophis refers to the speckled color pattern of serpents and the serpent-rock; others believed it was given the name because of its use as an antidote against snake venom. Dioscorides even recommended it for the prevention of snake bite. In 1546 the German physician and scientist Georgius Agricola latinized the name to *serpentenaria,* and this form became widely accepted. Our English word *serpentine* derived from the Latin. But the green rock is found worldwide: in Austria, Denmark, Germany, Norway, Sweden, and Switzerland it is *serpentin;* in Belgium it is *serpentine;* in Holland *serpentijn;* in Hungary there is *serpentinu; serpentina* in Rumania; and *serpentyn* in Poland. In Italy, Portugal, and Spain, the rock is called *serpentino.*

Naming usually gives the illusion that the thing named has been grasped, that it is defined, encompassed, circumscribed. Though named, the serpent-rock still snaked away from its namers, and confusion reigned over the nature of the serpentine/ophiolite. Across the Atlantic, American geologists added to the confusion. In a "Description of the Bare Hills Near Baltimore" in *Professor Silliman's Journal* (the *American Journal of Science*) of 1833, H. H. Hayden,

M.D., placed the rock under the classification of Brongniart's "ophiolite." (Hayden's straightforward description of the Bare Hills is sandwiched between meteorological notes from Fayettville, Vermont; an account of the collision of two comets; and a longer piece, "On Hybernation and Other Topics of Natural History," in which Judge Samuel Woodruff of Windsor, Connecticut, adds his contribution to the swallow debate by siding with those favoring torpid swallows in the mud.)

Professor Silliman's son-in-law and former student, James Dwight Dana, institutionalized the vagueness surrounding the term *ophiolite* by including it in his *Manual of Geology*, published in 1863. There under the "Hydrous Magnesian Series" of rocks, along with "talcose slate," "steatyte, or soapstone," "chlorite slate," and "serpentine" is "ophiolyte or verd-antique marble." Dana notes the occurrence often in "ophiolyte" of chrome and nickel, giving as examples the serpentines or ophiolytes of the Green Mountain Range, in those of Roxbury, Vermont; New Haven, Connecticut; Cornwall, England; Banffshire, Scotland; and Vosges, France. Though he acknowledged that no nickel was found from Easton, Pennsylvania (Lesley's puzzling Delaware River locality); Montville, New Jersey; and Newburyport, Massachusetts, he doesn't speculate on the distinction. "Ophiolyte" was "ophiolite," and "serpentine" was "serpentine"—the distinction of the two species of serpent-rocks awaited geologists with plate tectonic vision.

What kind of geologic vision existed in 1863? Dana's *Manual* is about as instructive about its time as any scientific publication might be. All of Archean time is presented there in a dozen pages, whereas the Paleozoic unfolds from brachiopods and trilobites through *Sauropus* and *Equiseta* in the course of some three hundred pages that follow. The Mesozoic fauna and flora are there: *Pterodactylus* and *Archaeopteryx*, *Sequoia* and *Palmicites*. The trap rock ridges of Dana's backyard—the lower Connecticut Valley, which was etched on a great Triassic basin—prick one's thoughts about the origins of the diabase hills, those traces of an opening Atlantic.

The Cenozoic, with its Tertiary Age of Mammals, and the Quaternary, with its Drift, finally delivered from the Wernerian deluge by Professor Agassiz, are in there too. And with it is the Age of Man, neatly split into the Paleolithic, Rheindeer, and Neolithic eras, with descriptions of the Paleozoic jawbone found in the Naulette Cave in Belgium next to bones of stags and marmots, wild boar and cave hyena. The caves of Perigord and Mentone are described with their Cro-Magnon men. A few pages past the Cro-Magnon skeletons are other species that were already gone by the late nineteenth century: the dodo, the moa, and the great auk. These are followed by prescient speculations about the buffalo and the giant sequoias.

The section that directly follows, "Changes in Levels of the Earth's Surface," is illustrated by a lithograph of the Temple of Jupiter Serapis at Pozzuoli, Italy. By this time, the British geologist Charles Lyell had already found barnacles on the rocks at Uddevalla, Sweden, 100 feet above the sea. Lyell had seen a lot of other truths, too, and partly sired by Lyell's book of new truths, *Principles of Geology*, the big truth, Darwin's *Origin of Species*, had been born and was all of four years old.

There is something disquieting about that lithograph of the Temple of Jupiter Serapis. Its message is hardly geological, though Dana intended it to be. The three remaining columns of the temple were shown to have been submerged by half their height, attested to by the lithodomic (rock-boring marine mollusks) holes 20 feet from the base of the columns. Dana based his description on that of Lyell, whose first volume of the *Principles* has an engraving of the Temple of Jupiter Serapis as the frontispiece. Lyell had visited the temple in 1828 and had, in true uniformitarian fashion, used the three surviving columns at Puzzuoli as "Proofs of the Elevation and Subsidence in the Bay of Baiae." The holes were incontrovertible evidence of past sea-level changes, the type of geological change that Lyell's observations showed had always occurred, and was still (*see Figure* 4).

Ideas and images spread. In America, the great geologic visionary landscape painter Thomas Cole (perhaps inspired by Lyell) drew a pencil sketch in 1832–33 titled *Ruins; or the Effects of Time* in which the sun sets behind a row of columns flanking the sea (*see Figure 5*). The disquieting truth is revealed by Cole's caption to his drawing:

Sun setting in the quiet ocean. Pyramids rising in the distance. Water & remains of stupendous edifices. The sea having encroached since they were erected. Broken mountains with huge rocks which seem to have descended from there and overturned columns in their downward course to the sea where a fragment is yet seen above the waves. A Bridge over the dry bed of a river. The river, having changed its course, flows a little distance. On

FIGURE 4   Frontispiece of Charles Lyell's *Principles of Geology*, showing the Temple of Jupiter Serapis at Puzzuoli, Italy

FIGURE 5   Sketch by Thomas Cole titled *Ruins; or, the Effects of Time* (1832–1833)

FIGURE 6   Frontispiece of J. D. Dana's *Manual of Geology*, showing Cro-Magnon skeleton from the cave of Mentone, France

the beach the wreck of a vessel. Broken aqueduct. In the foreground scattered trees. A fountain flowing into a broken cistern. The remains of a human skeleton in an uncovered sarcophagus. Broken swords, vases, &c.

The frontispiece of Dana's *Manual of Geology* is not the Temple of Jupiter Serapis, but it is equally haunting. It is an engraving of the skeleton of a Cro-Magnon from the cave of Mentone in France (*see Figure 6*). The skeleton is in fetal position, Mediterranean shells and flint implements lie all around, and a chaplet of stag's canines lies across his skull. Dana, Lyell, and the other nineteenth-century thinkers who grappled with deep time, though they may have erred in their understanding of geologic enigmas such as the serpentine, did not fail to see that man and his creations were ephemeral things.

Green Dreams

The elusive serpentine has slipped from our fingers again, leaving us to daydream about human things, about time and dust. But I know where to look for the serpent-rock, I know its haunts, and its tracks and traces, and I never tire of the search. We could head south, retracing our steps with a watchful eye for bare spots and stands of pitch pine, for house foundations of the mottled green stone, and cornerstones of steatite with the building's date inscribed. We could watch for talc dust rising into the air and look for outcrops of "asaxusas," with the markings of the quarry picks fading back into Archaic oblivion.

We'd leapfrog over Tyson's chromite prospect pits, scattered across the northern extensions of his Bare Hills, and pause at the great island river. We'd stand there at Bald Friar, the great black cliffs that were once covered with petroglyphs of shad and shamans (*see Figure 7*). The petroglyphs are gone now; those not blasted away and collecting dust in some museum basement are covered, along with the shad-run islands, by the waters behind the Conowingo Dam. Upstream lies the Peach Bottom Nuclear Power Plant. Herons fly along the edge of the river, 100 feet below.

Climb down from the high black knob and follow the railroad line downstream. The steeply dipping, contorted black beds of the phyllite and schist give way to a familiar green rock. Go and scratch it with your fingernail, feel its magnesian slipperiness. Look up to the place where the plants have found a foothold on the serpent-rock, and the red cedar and Virginia pine put down roots in the honeycomb rock soil. Look across the Susquehanna and see the horizon change—the canopy lowers, opens, and reveals those bare spots.

You are a river-islander, a proto-Susquehannock. You follow the tributaries of the great island river, and their tributaries. All orders of stream are known to you, down to the finger-width rivulets that

GENERAL VIEW OF THE "BALD FRIARS" SCULPTURED ROCKS IN THE SUSQUEHANNA RIVER. 1½ MILES SOUTH OF THE MARYLAND LINE. (Looking S.E.)

FIGURE 7   The petroglyphs at Bald Friar, along the Susquehanna River, circa 1880

are the outermost twigs of the branches of this watershed. If you were to follow the branch called Broad Creek, and trace it outward to Cunningham Branch, you'd find a little unnamed creek that at its source would be one of those outermost twigs. I'd meet you halfway up that twig, where a beech forest clothes the southern side of a ridge that runs down to the creek. I'd meet you in the boulder field that lies below the green greenness of the beech leaves of that forest.

The boulders are everywhere, grayish like the smooth bark of the beech trees. There are stumps of American chestnut, refusing decay. I'd see you there with your fellow river-islanders, engaged in the enterprise of quarrying the soft rock. I sit today under the beech trees and see you there. Unfinished bowls lie half buried in the matted layer of papery beech leaves that covers the ground. I find bowls with perfectly shaped lugs, the handles that had not occurred to that first bowl maker. There are "nodes" on the slope here, where I find quartz chippings and bowl fragments, and I see you there again, shaping the soft rock and dropping the pieces that will become my link to your Archaic present. I sit here and begin to know only about dugouts and creek highways, shad runs and huckleberry gathering.

As I wander along the slope and down by the creek, it is other refuse that jolts me out of my prehistoric musings. Rusted cables and old pots lie on the surface, awaiting the tens of centuries it will take to make them also half-buried artifacts (perhaps of more intense interest to some future wanderer). The rusted cables and square-sawn blocks of the soft rock speak of other enterprises, but they speak of enterprise all the same.

Head south once again. A mile along the way we pass a couple of metal buildings bearing the sign "Maryland Ceramic and Steatite Company." It's quitting time on a hot summer's day, but only a half dozen people file out to their cars. A couple of years ago there would have been four dozen people punching the time clock. The Maryland Ceramic and Steatite Company quarried talc from a soapstone ridge out back behind the buildings. It was a special high-grade talc that was quarried, perfect for use in electrical insulators. It was perfect for the prehistoric inhabitants of this area too, and when the Harford Talc Company (now Maryland Ceramic and Steatite) began quarrying the talc here, the quarrymen would often find soapstone bowls, cups, pendants, and quartz quarry picks and chisels.

There are bowl fragments on a metal shelf in the cluttered office of

Spook Dinning, the fourth generation of Dinnings to operate the company. He'll show you the row after row of odd little contemporary artifacts, this one to go in an aquarium, that one in a speaker or table lamp. He'll tell you how the cream-colored insulators are ones made with talc from out back, and how the darker ones are made with steatite from Africa, where at the day's end the black quarry-men are as white as snow from the talc dust. There are no health and safety regulations in the African quarry, the kind of regulations that Dinning says forced him to close the quarry out back and put forty people out of work.

Go on through Darlington, Maryland, where the Protestant Episcopal Church is all of serpentine stone, quarried from the Broad Creek Quarry, a short walk over a small serpentine barren from the boulder field under the beech trees on that unnamed creek. You are a geologist. You pass towns that have familiar names, being the type localities of geologic formations that define the Piedmont here. There are Port Deposit, Cockeysville, and Glenarm. The serpentine is nameless, but its traces are always there, in the soapstone ridges and the barren spots.

The serpentine band that began up in Chester County tapers around the Gunpowder River and dissolves into disjunct spots along the Piedmont. The most conspicuous is "Soldier's Delight," a protected barrens of about 2,000 acres. The day I was there I met a man who worked for the Maryland Parks Department. I asked him what he knew about the barrens, about Tyson's mining efforts there, and about people's feelings about the barrens. He didn't say much, but he said I ought to talk to this fellow he knew, who was one of the twelve survivors of a collapse in the main chromite mine, years back. Where was this man and how could I get in touch with him? "He's ninety-six now, and he's just gone into a nursing home. He's not well." History is always slipping away.

But the adits are still there, fenced now to keep out the curious. In the naked serpentine walls above the rotting timbers that support the adit entrance grows the little ebony spleenwort, *Asplenium trichomanes*, its roots lying next to the pods of chromite that were Tyson's quarry. There are prospect pits scattered throughout the Virginia pine–blackjack oak–post oak woods. In the bare areas that alternate with these woods there grow the tough depauperate serpentine plants: the lyre-leaved rock cress, the hairy mouse-ear chickweed, slender knotweed, and the fameflower. On warm summer days the calls of towhees and prairie warblers are heard here, and at night there are whippoorwills.

Head south again. Almost all the little barren fragments and soapstone ridge traces are lost under that "ruthless invasion of suburban improvement" that William Henry Holmes lamented in 1925. Just beyond lies Washington, D.C., the Marcey Creek site above Little Falls, Soapstone Valley, and Holmes's collections. And south we might continue, via the soapstone quarries of the Archaic peoples of the James River Basin, and the big quarries at Schuyler, Virginia, and south still, over the less serpentinized olivine and dunite deposits at North Carolina and Georgia.

We might end our search here, call it quits not far from the Savannah River, southeast of the southern end of the Blue Ridge, close to where the Appalachians finally dive back under the Coastal Plain. There on the slopes of Burks Mountain we'd find the southern Piedmont's version of a small serpentine barren, with open parklike stands of blackjack oak, post oak, and longleaf and shortleaf pines, all of which have wandered off their usual habitats on the sandy Coastal Plain. These xeric trees grow over the erect clematis, *Clematis albicoma*, whose home is on the shale barrens of Virginia, and the rattlesnake master, *Agave virginica*, with its thick, fleshy leaves in a rosette below the six-foot flower stalk. The flowers are fragrant, especially at night, when the whippoorwill calls. We'll head north instead, past the barrens of Chester County, past the barns of serpentine with black Triassic diabase trim, past shopping center parking lots that are slippery where the magnesian stone is eroding off new, unvegetated slopes. We will pass the many nineteenth-century houses and churches built of the green rock, past West Chester, where the green walls of Joseph Brinton's quarry (*see Figure 8*) are reflected in the pool of water that now serves as a swim club. It's best to search on rainy days when the serpentine's color is renewed, like a snake that has just shed its dusty skin. Adjacent to Brinton's quarry there is a road called "Serpentine Drive," where the suburban landscape is underlain by serpentine rubble from the quarry, where a frog carved out of serpentine marks one of the driveway entrances, and where the eccentric frog sculptor squirrels away promising blocks from Brinton's quarry at crossroads, returning later to release the forms hidden in the green stone. Serpentine brings out the sculptor in people—it somehow begs to be shaped or inscribed. A half mile from the quarry is a building that was once

FIGURE 8   Joseph Brinton's serpentine quarry, circa 1882

called "Darlington's Inn," which bears a serpentine date-stone inscribed "1823." It also bears other marks, the profile of Henry Clay,
carved by David Taylor (an ardent West Chester Whig) in 1844 when
Clay was running for president. Facing Clay is the likeness of Taylor's
dog, "Abe," which Taylor chiseled in 1860 when Abraham Lincoln was
a presidential candidate.

Closer to Philadelphia, suburbia and urbia further obscure the
trail, but it can still be found. The serpentine stone from Brinton's
quarry in the buildings at the University of Pennsylvania is being
eaten away by the sulfuric-acid-laden atmosphere. At the Old State
House (Independence Hall), it was two centuries of footsteps, not
sulfuric acid, that ate away the soapstone steps, steps that the members of the Second Continental Congress—the radicals Benjamin
Franklin, John Adams, James Madison, Thomas Jefferson, John
Hancock, Patrick Henry, and Paul Revere—ascended in 1775.

The trail has surprising turns. I went to the offices of Independence National Historical Park to find out where the soapstone was

quarried, but no one could tell me. I was leaving when a man walked in and I asked him. Sure he knew where the soapstone had come from—his father had been foreman of the quarry. But this man had a southern accent. . . . He told me how the original steps had been replaced a few years back, and that the soapstone had come from the Alberene quarries at Schuyler, Virginia. His grandfather had worked in the quarries for sixty-two years and had done about every job there was to do in the quarries and millworks. When Harry Truman remodeled the fireplace mantels in the White House with black steatite from Schuyler, this man's grandfather did the work. He told me how his uncle, Colonel Earl Hamner, had cut wood for the boilers at the Alberene plant, how the Grandpa character in the TV series "The Waltons" was based on Earl, except they'd changed it so he carved wood instead of cutting cordwood. He showed me a little block of soapstone on his desk.

But where did the original soapstone in Independence Hall come from? It apparently came from Prince's quarry, on the Schuylkill, just north of the city. This was the section of the Schuylkill that was Henry Roger's "window," the window to understanding the nature of the crystalline Appalachians, the window that ultimately opened onto nowhere.

The thin green traces that marked Rogers's "Azoic" rocks re-appear here just east of the Schuylkill, on the banks of the Wissa-hickon Creek. Besides the outcrop (up on the bank where few notice it), there are two huge blocks of steatite that flank Bell's Mill Road where it crosses the "Wissy." It's a stopping place, and the steatite blocks are convenient to lean upon for the many passersby. More than a few of those passersby have "discovered" the soft stone's properties and have left their initials scratched in the rock. Perhaps some of the same people have wandered up Bell's Mill Road to Ger-mantown Road, and down through the boutiquey section on Chest-nut Hill. Perhaps they've wandered into the Touchstone Gallery, intrigued by the Eskimo sculpture and prints displayed in the win-dow. Perhaps they've done more than just covet these artifacts of another world, perhaps they've been educated by the proprietor, learned that soapstone carving by the Eskimo goes back thousands of years, to a time when stone lamps were made to provide light and heat in the long Arctic night. They could learn, too, that stone bowls and miniature carved reproductions of tools were made from the soft rock, the miniatures being placed in the graves of the dead in the belief that they could later be enlarged to their natural size. And just as today there is art in soapstone to bring money and life into Arctic communities, a thousand years ago there had been earlier stone art, created with the soft stone, the "touchstone." But maybe none of the wanderers who have touched the stone down on the Wissahickon know that it was quarried by the original people of their own backyard, the proto-Susquehannock, the Lenape, and others. Just as they scratched the soft rock with their fingernails, so had the canoe-wanderers three thousand years before. There are many ghosts down there by the Wissahickon: the talc traces left by your hand were left by their hands.

Ochee Springs

There are other ghosts along this Appalachian trail, and I never fail to encounter them. I've met the ghosts of prehistoric quarry-men farther north, at the Ochee Springs quarry in Rhode Island. There, surrounded by concrete, is a steatite outcrop a few meters wide that bears ovoid scars like the ones seen by W. H. Holmes at the Connecticut Avenue quarries in Washington, D.C. (*see Figure 9*). The entire outcrop is pitted with the concavities that supplied some unknown people with stone bowls. Until about ten years ago, there were short "stems" of stone that projected up from the center of the hollows—these were the unneeded "centers" left by the quarrymen. These have all been knocked off by vandals, and many of the depressions now are receptacles for soda cans and fast-food wrappings. The fine mineral spring that once drew the people here thousands of years ago (the water was bottled and sold to Providence-area residents earlier in this century) is now befouled and dry.

The Ochee Springs quarry was discovered in 1878, when workmen on the Horatio Angell "Big Elm Tree Farm" in Johnston, Rhode Island, exposed the earth-covered steatite ledge. It was the first prehistoric soapstone quarry in New England to come to the attention of the emerging professional archaeological community. After its discovery, both private collectors and representatives from museums and universities throughout New England descended on the site, and over three hundred cartloads of chipping debris, unfinished bowls, slate and quartzite quarry picks, abraders, and hammerstones were hauled away. Frederick Ward Putnam, then director of the Peabody Museum at Harvard, visited the quarry with Professor J.W.P. Jenks of Brown University and H. N. Angell, the owner, and reported on the site and its artifacts later that year.

At the time of Putnam's visit, over two thousand rude stone chisels had been found on the steatite ledge; most of them had been carted a

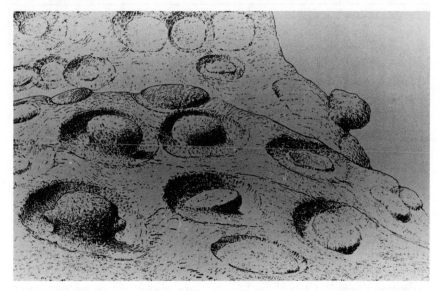

FIGURE 9   W. H. Holmes's drawing of aboriginal steatite quarry at Clifton, Virginia

few hundred yards away to be used as fill for a low marshy piece of land. The chisels were all of nearly the same size, chipped to a blunt point at one end and roughly rounded to fit the hand at the other. They varied in length from 5 to 8½ inches, and in weight from 1 to 4 pounds, and were made from the hard stone of adjoining ledges. Putnam, like Holmes, instinctively tried the chisels out on the soap-stone and found how easily the steatite could be worked by these rough implements.

In one limited area of the steatite ledge, measuring 15 feet long, 8 wide, and 6 deep, there was evidence of the removal of sixty "pot-forms." Putnam estimated that three or four hundred pots had prob-ably been made from the substance of this one small area, and that the entire ledge had supplied several thousand. Confronted with the massive workings here, Putnam made the same inference anyone might have—either the soapstone pots were once in great demand, or their manufacture here had spanned a number of centuries. As with the questions posed by Holmes, the answers would not come until eight decades later, with the technique of radiocarbon dating.

Besides the question of the age of the quarry, Putnam briefly pon-dered the problem that intrigued most nineteenth-century archaeol-ogists—the nature of soapstone vessels as articles of trade. For many years before the discovery of the first eastern quarry, steatite artifacts had been found all over the area east of the Mississippi, many of them far from any possible source of stone. Their occurrence in New England being more common than elsewhere, Putnam believed that region to be the center of an aboriginal trade network.

As American archaeology widened its scope of activity, the flurry of professional interest in the steatite quarries along the Appalachians waned, and relics from Central America and the Pacific began to fill the shelves in New England museums. Aside from the excavation of a quarry in Connecticut by F. H. Saville for the Peabody Museum in 1892, it was not until the 1930s and 1940s that archaeological attention returned to the New England steatite workings. The catalyst for this attention was William S. Fowler, who directed excavation at the Westfield quarry near the Little River in Westfield, Massachusetts, during the years 1937 to 1940.

At Westfield, the familiar evidence for stone bowl production was abundant, but more important, about 100 yards away from the steatite quarry was found a quartz tool quarry. There, in front of a group of boulders with an exposed outcropping of crystalline quartz, Fowler and his associates excavated an area of about 90 square feet and found tailings of quartz dust up to 2 feet deep. About five hundred rechipped artifacts were found among the tailings, their toollike shapes and proximity to the steatite quarry suggesting that they were intended for use as steatite-working tools.

During the course of the excavation, three tool caches were located in deep excavated crevices in a quartz boulder. Within the caches, over one hundred carefully worked tools were found. After experimenting with the tools, Fowler classified them into eight types: "rocker abraders," triangular tools used to hollow out the larger bowls; "scraping chisels," used to reduce the thickness of the walls and bottoms; "shavers," small razor-edged pieces that enabled the worker to produce thin, even walls without danger of fracture and whose rounded end neatly cut out the curve at the foot of the inside walls of the bowl; "abrading scrapers," whose roughly chipped cutting edge suggests that it was probably worked back and forth like a saw; "pipe reamers," for cutting pipe bowls; "drills" and "bits," for making holes; "end picks" and "corner picks," for gouging the inside of the quarry blank; and "hand gouges," for further roughing out of the bowl interior.

Fowler was impressed with the fact that in one of the three caches the tools were so carefully packed that it was difficult to dislodge them without causing breakage. To Fowler, this was not the work of an individual who came only infrequently to flake out tools as he needed them, but that of trained tool makers who were building up a surplus of tools in their leisure moments. Fowler also believed that the tools he found at the Westfield quarry, being more highly specialized than those of the Potomac Valley and neighboring regions, suggested a beginning date for the New England steatite "industry" that was more ancient than that of the southern Appalachians.

Just what was the beginning date, and what was the overall time span of the industry? Before the 1950s all that could be done was to connect domestic stone artifacts when found in quarry workings with known culture periods then being studied. The diagnostic artifacts were projectile points—"arrowheads" to the layperson, though few ever adorned an arrow—which at the time were treated as equivalent to geological index fossils in archaeological stratigraphy.

The occurrence of projectile points at steatite quarries was quite rare, though, probably restricted to occasional loss from individual tool kits down through the centuries. In 1948, however, Fowler excavated the Ragged Mountain quarry in Connecticut, which proved to be a steatite quarry and rock shelter all in one. This is the only time that such a combination of domestic living and industrial activity had been uncovered, and projectile points were abundant in the tailings of the quarry living area. The points found were diagnostic of the late Archaic, including Eared, Small Triangular #4, Corner-Removed #7, and Side-Notched #1 types. (This is only a small sampling of the jargon of projectile point typology. There are Folsom points, Hardaway Side-Notched, Kirk Corner-Notched, Le Croy Stemmed, Neville, Stark, and Merrimack points, Jacks Reef Pentagonal, Adena and Levanna points, and many more.)

The first accurate carbon-14 date from a steatite quarry was reported in 1957 at the Horne Hill quarry near Millbury, Massachusetts. There, a radiocarbon date of 2,730 ± 120 years ago was obtained of a charcoal sample from a stone hearth buried 7 feet deep in quarry tailings. The 7 feet of tailings above the hearth was interpreted to represent a thousand years of time, and as the hearth was interpreted by Fowler to represent approximately the middle of the quarry's life span, this indicated a working period of about two thousand years, with a starting date of thirty-seven hundred years ago. In 1971 Fowler's estimate was partially confirmed by charcoal from a hearth at the Harlan Mill steatite quarry in Delaware, which yielded a date of 3380 ± 160 years.

Despite the advent of radiocarbon dating, the questions of both the beginning date and the overall time span of the steatite "industry" are not conclusively answered, since the dates differ slightly along the Appalachians. As in the Potomac and Susquehanna drainage basins, steatite bowls in New England drop out of the archaeological record with the coming of ceramics, which reached southern New England around 700 B.C., and only a few centuries B.C. in the north. What seems to have happened is something that holds true for all innovations in all human cultures through all of history and prehistory—when the cultural system of any group of people makes the adoption of a new technology advantageous, they adopt it. Though the innovation of the soapstone bowl appeared at different times along the length of the Appalachians, it did so only because of the underlying cultural imperative—the need for durable and efficient cookware. The replacement of steatite technology by ceramics came about via the same process.

Mystery Pendants
on the Missisquoi

While archaeologists from Holmes to Putnam to Fowler have had to dig deep in their own musings on the steatite workers of the Terminal Archaic, there is yet another soapstone mystery that reaches even deeper into time and demands poetry, not science. In 1922, in East Highgate, Vermont, two amateur archaeologists, William Ross and Benjamin Fisher, discovered over two hundred stone artifacts in a thin layer of yellowish sand at a place that has come to be known as the Reagan site. Included among the artifacts from this site are fifteen objects, three of soapstone and the rest of talc, which are unlike anything ever found at any other contemporaneous site in North America.

The Reagan site stands on a high, sandy bluff, 8 miles from Missisquoi Bay of Lake Champlain. From the site one looks south and west over the broad valley of the Missisquoi River, which lies three-quarters of a mile away and some 300 feet below. When Ross and Fisher discovered the site, the forest of white pine that held the sand in place had recently been cut down, and a few months of wind had revealed the tools that had lain buried for some ten thousand years.

Ten thousand years ago, the Missisquoi River did not lie three-quarters of a mile away, meandering through its broad valley. This valley was an arm of the Champlain Sea then, and the marine waters of that sea sorted and deposited the sand that made this beach, which stands some 500 feet above sea level. The sea had first formed around 11,800 B.C., during the waning stages of the Pleistocene. As the Pleistocene ice retreated to the north, two important events were occurring—sea level was rising as water was set free from its glacial prison, and the land was rebounding from having been depressed by the weight of the ice sheet. Eleven thousand years ago, the ice had left the Saint Lawrence Valley, but the rebound of the land had not kept pace with the rising sea level, permitting the entry of seawater from the proto-Gulf of Saint Lawrence into the Champlain Valley and its tributaries.

The people who camped along this ancient strand were Paleo-Indians, known from all over North America by their distinctive fluted points (frequently called "Clovis" points, after the site in New Mexico where the remains were first identified). Paleo-Indians were big-game hunters, and in Vermont during Champlain Sea time, the people probably hunted the now-extinct wooly mammoth, woodland caribou, and musk ox, as well as modern species of elk, deer, moose, and wolf. The marine waters of the Champlain Sea provided a different though bountiful sort of game: beluga, finback, and bowhead whales; ringed, harp, and hooded seals; harbor porpoises; and perhaps walrus.

The fluted points and gravers and scrapers from the Reagan site are made of chert, jasper, quartzite and rhyolite, some of it local, some exotic. They are utilitarian objects that speak of the material economy of a very ancient people. They tell us nothing of the beliefs, the fears, or the ideas of these big-game hunters. The fifteen soapstone and talc objects from the Reagan site are not utilitarian objects. Most of them are only 2 or 3 inches in length and have holes drilled in them, apparently so that they could be worn as pendants. Many of them look like ornaments, and a number of them are marked by grooved lines. Perhaps these were prehistoric "worry stones," kept in the Paleo hunter's tool kit to be fondled during contemplative moments. Paleo-Indian hunters had children; perhaps these soft stones are trinkets made by a father for his daughter or son.

Paleo-Indians saw lightning and the aurora borealis, heard thunder and probably music; they witnessed birth and death, they knew sickness and they knew joy. That band of hunters on a beach of the Champlain Sea must have wondered about who they were, where they came from, and where they were going. Though indecipherable to us, these fifteen pieces of soft rock—"asaxusas"—were once charged with meaning, animated with the beliefs that made them human, and make us human.

The closest source of steatite for the Paleo-Indian band that left those mystery pendants is upriver, where the Missisquoi first pulls itself together out of the streams that run down from the Lowell Mountains and the low hills that lie between the Lowell Range and the main ridge of the Green Mountains to the west. In this upper part of the Missisquoi Valley, there are dozens of possible sources of steatite, mostly along the borders of the ultramafic plutons that intrude the schists of the Hazens Notch and Stowe formations. The relation of the steatite and the ultramafic plutons to the country rock here is complicated, but recent geological work has brought a revelation that seems as fantastic as the myths that the ancients on that beach told one another in the ten-thousand-year-old night: that the earth's skin moves about, it is born and consumed in great megacycles, and in the process continents collide, mountains are lifted out of the sea, and ocean crust comes to rest in places like the Upper Missisquoi, to provide soft stone for prehistoric peoples, asbestos for a thriving group of newcomers, and islands of refuge for a suite of very particular plants.

The Emergence of Plate Tectonics

In 1912 a German meteorologist named Alfred Wegener put forth the theory that the continents on either side of the Atlantic—the North American and South American continents and the European-African continent—were once joined and that they had split and drifted apart into their present positions. He also believed that the other continents were also joined, making one giant proto-continent named Pangaea. Like Darwin and the theory of evolution, Wegener's theory, termed "continental drift," had been around for a century or more, but in incomplete and sometimes wholly incorrect form. Also like Darwin, Wegener's unique life experience brought him to a point where he could marshal more evidence for his theory and present it in such a way that it would not be taken as the ravings of a crackpot.

The first intimation of continental drift had come to Wegener around Christmas in 1910, while he was perusing an atlas. He noticed, as had others before him, that the outlines of the continents fit together like the pieces of a jigsaw puzzle, but he dismissed this as trivial evidence of a highly improbable idea. A year later Wegener accidentally came across a group of writings describing the faunal similarities of Paleozoic rock strata in Africa and Brazil. To account for the similarities, the authors had taken up the notion of a former land bridge across the Atlantic, but to Wegener, this was evidence of continental linkage, and he was stirred to investigate the idea further. Within four months (in 1910) he presented his hypothesis to the Geological Association of Frankfurt-am-Main in an address titled "The Geophysical Basis of the Evolution of the Large-Scale Features of the Earth's Crust (Continents and Oceans)."

The prevailing notion of the earth through the late nineteenth and early twentieth centuries had of course been one of permanency of continents and ocean basins, and its most illustrious champion was none other than James Dwight Dana. Dana believed that the continents and oceans were broadly delineated at the beginning of geologic time and were permanent features of the earth's crust. The movement that did occur, according to Dana, occurred due to global contraction as the earth cooled from its once-molten state. When Dana proposed the "doctrine of permanence," he described the ocean floors as more contracted, hence denser, than the continental bedrock. Global contraction had, he believed, forced the crust into great folds: a downfold ("geosynclinal") adjacent to the land, bordered on the seaward side by an upfold ("geanticlinal"). The geosynclinal was eventually filled with sediments eroded from the geanticlinal, then uplifted.

This homegrown Appalachian geosynclinal theory had its origin in the work of James Hall of the New York Survey. Hall had noticed that the Paleozoic sediments of western New York (and farther west in Iowa, where he had also studied) were thin, whereas those of the Appalachian area were very thick; yet their fossil assemblages indicated that each had formed during about the same span of time. Hall reasoned that there must be a causal relationship between the greater thickness of sediments in the Appalachians and their mountainous character. His conclusion was that all large mountain chains must represent areas of great accumulation of sediments, being basins that gradually subsided as they filled. Later, these great sedimentary prisms were uplifted, then eroded into the mountain belts we see today. In true uniformitarian spirit, Hall had worked out a theory of orogenesis (mountain formation) based on slow surficial processes—those of erosion and sedimentation.

To Dana, Hall's theory was unsatisfactory, being "a theory of the origin of mountains with the mountains left out." Hall was a true field man, and any theories that made their way into his reports were incidental to his observations. Dana was the real theorist, and in 1873 he discussed Hall's sediment-filled basins (Dana's own geosynclinals) in an article in the *American Journal of Science* titled "On Some Results of Earth Contraction from Cooling." Here, Dana interpreted the geosynclinals as tectonic basins forced downward by compression during the earth's cooling phase, those basins being filled with shallow water sediments as a result of subsidence, not causing it.

Dana's theory of mountain building led directly to a theory of continent building, since the train of crustal folds was envisioned to press landward over time, as the basins and their sedimentary infill were arched upward, then welded to the continent as a coastal mountain range. Where else but North America, with its flanks of coastal mountains, could such a theory of continental accretion have been produced?

Between Dana's doctrine of permanence and Wegener's continental drift there came the thoughts of an Austrian, Edward Suess, whose four-volume work *Das Antlitz der Erde* (The Face of the Earth) was published between 1885 and 1909. While rejecting the doctrine of permanence, Suess believed, as had Dana, in the "wrinkled apple" model—that global contraction from cooling was the fundamental cause of all geologic structures. But this was before Marie Curie had found that the element radium produced heat as well as radiation during the decay process called radioactivity, and also before Lord Rayleigh and others had detected radioactivity in earth materials from all over the world. The earth was not cooling at all, for it had an internal, continuous heat source.

Suess's contribution to this epic geopoem was his particular model of a contracting earth, for two of the terms he coined became central to later thinkers. Suess saw the earth as being composed of three concentric shells: the "nife" (abbreviated from the chemical terms for the elements nickel, Ni, and iron, Fe), which was the core; the "sima" (abbreviating silica-magnesium), being the mantle; and the "sal" (silica-aluminum), or crust. Wegener later (1924) changed this last term to "sial."

Suess thought that the sial had once covered the entire earth, but that shrinkage of the earth's core caused immense slabs of it to founder into the magnesian mantle below, thus creating ocean basins. Wegener, on the other hand, knew this to be impossible, since the sial was less dense than the sima and, like a floe of ice, would remain on top. It was already known in Wegener's day that the earth's sialic crust could be depressed or elevated; the most striking example was the well-documented postglacial uplift of Scandinavia after the retreat of the ice sheet. Like earlier continental drift proponents, Wegener believed that lateral as well as vertical movement of the crust was possible, and like them, he needed a force capable of initiating such movement.

Unlike his predecessors, Wegener avoided conjuring some catastrophic event such as the rupturing of the moon from the earth's spleen, which was one of the popular nineteenth-century notions, to initiate continental drift. He proposed instead two forces that were derived from the earth's rotation—the Eotvos, or pole-fleeing force, and lunar-solar tidal drag on a viscous earth. The problem with these forces is that they are not catastrophic enough, and geophysicists repeatedly showed this to the scientific community. Partially because of this lack of a motive force, and partially because of the reluctance of scientists to accept the idea of a mobile earth surface, the theory of continental drift, born in 1912, was virtually dead by the 1930s.

One force considered by Wegener, and also by others before him, was that caused by convection currents in the mantle. This hypothesis suggests that the mantle of the earth undergoes thermal convection similar to that seen in a kettle of soup on a stove: as the soup at the bottom is heated it expands and, becoming less dense, it rises to the top. The problem with this model, however, is that the earth's mantle is more like porridge than soup. Porridge will burn at the bottom while it is still cool a few inches away from the top, since the temperature gradient is not enough to overcome the high viscosity (that is, "stickiness") of the porridge. Like porridge, the mantle is highly viscous, and opponents of the mantle convection hypothesis pointed out that the model was inadequate. Despite these objections, a number of confirmed "drifters" embraced the mantle convection model, wedding it with Wegener's theory of continental drift. Arthur Holmes, a radioactivity specialist from Edinburgh and Cambridge universities, was perhaps the most vocal proponent of such a view. He asserted that convective flow was sufficient to carry along a continent, and he likened the flow to "an endless travelling belt."

That was 1931. Alfred Wegener had died the previous autumn, out on the Greenland ice cap, pursuing clues to support his hypothesis. With Wegener gone, and despite such skillful advocates of continental drift as Arthur Holmes and Alexander du Toit of Johannesburg, South Africa, the drift hypothesis became the laughing stock of the geological community. Paleontologists told satirical tales of finding half of a certain fossil in Newfoundland and the other half in Ireland, while skeptical geology professors drew nonsensical paleogeographic maps on blackboards.

The next three decades saw significant progress in deep-sea geophysics, progress that shifted attention to the ocean floor, particularly at the site of mid-oceanic ridges. Such ridges were suspected during the mid-nineteenth century when the first submarine cable was being laid across the Atlantic. (The ridges were called the "Telegraphic Plateau" at the time.) Later studies showed the "plateau" to extend practically the length of the Atlantic, and since then similar mid-oceanic ridges have been discovered in the Pacific and Indian oceans. These ridges are more than 3,000 meters high and over 2,000 kilometers wide, surpassing the Himalayas in scale. At the same time, grand depressions or "trenches" (some 3,200 kilometers long and 11 kilometers deep, ten times the depth and length of the Grand Canyon) were being discovered on the ocean floor.

With this new knowledge in place, the concept of continental drift underwent a sort of reincarnation. In 1962 Harry Hess of Princeton University published a paper titled "History of the Ocean Basins," in which he proposed that the mid-oceanic ridges are formed over the rising limbs of convection cells in the mantle, and that when these limbs reach the surface they spread laterally to either side in the manner of Holmes's "conveyor belts." Believing that the mantle is predominantly peridotite, an extremely dense silicate rock that is rare in continental crust, Hess proposed that heated waters brought up with the rising limbs of the convection cells reacted with the peridotite to form serpentinite (this process had been proved experimentally in the laboratory). Riding along on the conveyor belt at the bottom of the ocean, the serpentinite rind became blanketed with marine sediments before plunging down again into the mantle at the trenches. There the rind was reheated, the captured water was expelled into the ocean, and the serpentinite was transformed into peridotite. The blanket of sediments rode down into the trench, where it was heated, partially metamorphosed, then welded to the continent.

With a single agency, Hess explained the youth of the ocean floors (discovered from deep-sea dredging and coring to be nowhere greater than about two hundred million years old), the source of ocean water on the planet, the origin of mid-oceanic ridges and trenches, and continental accretion. Hess also explained continental drift, imagining that where the convection cells rose under continents the sialic crust was split open, and the pieces were carried aside at equal rates. The continents were not, as Wegener believed, independently propelled, plowing like great sialic ships through a yielding ocean floor. Instead, Hess proposed, the continents were rafts frozen onto, and carried by, a rigid but moving sea floor. Robert S. Dietz, toying with the same idea at almost the same time, named the process "sea-floor spreading."

With some additional geological evidence (mostly from studies of the remanent magnetism—the permanent magnetization induced by the earth's magnetic field—of the sea floor) in place, by 1968 there emerged from a century of hypotheses, refutations, and rethinking a new view of the earth, called by geologists the "new global tectonics" or "plate tectonics." Biology had been delivered its organizing principle in 1859, with the publication of Darwin's *Origin of Species*—now geology had its own organizing principle.

Plate tectonics proposes a model in which the earth is currently divided into eight to twelve rigid but shifting plates, each about 100 kilometers thick. Most of the plates support at least one massive continental plateau, referred to as a craton. Along one edge of each plate there is usually a subduction zone where the plate dives into the earth's mantle, sometimes reaching a depth of as much as 700 kilometers before being resorbed. (These subduction zones are marked by the trenches discovered earlier.) The opposite side of the plate is marked by a mid-oceanic rift, from which the crust consumed at the trench is renewed by the inflow of liquid basalt and quasi-solid mantle rock. Completing this geometry are transform faults that accommodate plate motion by moving horizontally, permitting the plates to move without consuming or generating new crust.

Three types of plate boundaries are thus possible: divergent junctures (the mid-oceanic rifts where new ocean crust is created), megashears (the transform faults where the plates slip laterally past one another; the San Andreas Fault is such a feature), and convergent junctures (the trenches where two plates collide, with one plate being subducted and consumed). It is here at the convergent juncture that the dramas of the "old geology"—geosynclinals, orogenesis, and continental accretion—are enacted.

Since Hall's and Dana's day, the concept of the geosyncline had taken on new meaning, and also a new lack of meaning, as geologists named dozens of different "species" of geosynclines. Parageosynclines, paraliogeosynclines, orthogeosynclines, taphrogeosynclines, epieugeosynclines, and others proliferated, and so did confusion. Two terms of genuine utility to geologists have emerged from the double-talk: "miogeosyncline" (sometimes shortened to miogeocline, since they aren't truly synclinal) and "eugeosyncline," or eugeocline. Miogeoclines are essentially continental shelfs formed along the margins of the continental platforms on sialic, continental crust. After a basal sequence of nonmarine to marine clastics—conglomerates, arkoses, and shales—deposited in the late Precambrian rift basins as the continental plates began to split, the Appalachian miogeocline was deposited as a great carbonate sequence—limestones and dolomites—some 3,000 meters thick, laid down in shallow waters from the lower Cambrian on through the Middle Ordovician. The sediments laid down in the early Paleozoic miogeosyncline that flanked the North American plate are now found in the Ridge and Valley Province of the Appalachians (the "Folded Appalachians").

Southeast of the early Paleozoic carbonates are the eugeosynclinal deposits, their division marked by great uplifts of basement rocks— the Blue Ridge in Virginia, the Green Mountains in Vermont, and the Long Range in Newfoundland. These uplifts mark the imaginary "Blue-Green-Long Line" to Appalachian geologists. The eugeosynclinal deposits are of a very different nature, consisting of sediments laid down on simatic, oceanic crust, or extended and thinned continental crust. These rocks are equivalent to modern-day examples of continental rise deposits such as those found on continental margins bordering the Atlantic Ocean. The cherts, slates, greywackes, and the like that make up these deposits have been strongly deformed, metamorphosed, and plutonized, such that only within the last few decades have they really been understood. These are the rocks that once belonged to the "Archean" realm of nineteenth-century thought.

The deformation of these rocks we now know, thanks to the concepts of plate tectonics, was due to the rifting apart of crustal plates and their subsequent collision. The initial rift developed before the beginning of the Paleozoic, and it marked the edge of the North American continental plate, where the craton fell away to a broad new oceanic domain. (This proto-Atlantic Ocean is called "Iapetus," after the father of the god Atlantis of Greek mythology.)

Beginning in the Middle Paleozoic, the opposing continental plates converged, and their collision is recorded by a succession of Appalachian orogenies—the Taconic in the north, then the Acadian, and others later farther south (for example, the Alleghenian)— that make up the Appalachian orogen. By the middle Paleozoic, the deep basin that was the eugeosyncline had become a highland area that shed detritus westward onto the miogeosyncline, and then, in a grand denouement, mobility gradually diminished in the former eugeosynclinal area. Much later, in the late Triassic, rifting commenced again, producing the tensional grabens that filled with sediment to become the red sandstone regions of the Connecticut Valley and Newark Basin. While dinosaurs ambled through these red beds, the Atlantic was reopened, as the Appalachians drifted west to their present position. The craton onto which they were welded still drifts westward with its subjoined plate, its leading edge experiencing earthquakes, while its trailing edge, the Atlantic Coastal Plain and continental shelf, continues to receive sediments as an active miogeocline. Out beyond the edge of the shelf, detritus drifts deep to blanket the ocean crust.

The eugeosyncline to the east today stands as a mountain belt, old and eroded, but now mostly demystified by the new organizing principle. Mostly demystified, for in among the ensiatic rocks that were once deep-water deposits, there still lay a green ensimatic mystery.

Ophiolites

One of the first geologic problems to yield new solutions within the framework of plate tectonics was the "ophiolite problem." When we last left the term *ophiolite*, it had just been coined by Alexandre Brongniart of France as an alternative name for serpentinite. During the late nineteenth and early twentieth centuries, European and American mineralogists and petrologists arbitrarily extended the term so that it had little real meaning. However, in 1927 Gustav Steinmann of Germany elevated ophiolite from a rock term to a rock association term, by placing peridotites (including serpentine), gabbro, diabase, spillite, and related rocks in a kindred relationship. Steinmann had earlier noted the occurrence of this assemblage in the Apennines, the Alpine fold mountains that make up the spine of the Italian peninsula.

At the time, Steinmann emphasized the association between deep-water sediments capping the ophiolite and the underlying serpentinite and pillow lavas, basaltic lavas that have been extruded into water (this association eventually became known as "Steinmann's Trinity"). This led to the proposal by others that ophiolites were masses of igneous rock emplaced in the early stages of eugeosyncline development. They believed that the igneous rocks were either intruded into the layers of sedimentary rock as sills (horizontal intrusions), or that they were huge balloons of molten rock erupted onto the surface of deep-water eugeosynclinal sediments.

The philosophical underpinning of the eugeosynclinal model of Steinmann's Trinity is that the rocks were autochthonous, that is, formed in situ, whether intruded as sills or spilled out over the surface. It is this concept that has been radically altered since the advent of the new global tectonics. Today, almost all ophiolite masses are viewed as allochthonous, that is, they were formed elsewhere and were transported tectonically to their current resting place.

Instead of magmatic intrusions or extrusions, ophiolites are now viewed as pieces of oceanic crust that formed along the mid-oceanic ridge, moved across the ocean floor via the conveyor belt of sea-floor spreading, then finally were thrust over or into ("obducted") a continental margin.

It has been calculated that less than one ten-thousandth of a percent of all oceanic crust has been obducted onto dry land, yet this small remnant provides unique clues about the evolution of ancient oceans and the mechanisms of collisions between plates. These exhumed bits of oceanic crust also mark the locations of those collisions—they are "geosutures" of enormous proportions (*see Map* 4). As with so many recent breakthroughs in earth science, the information that sparked this new interpretation came from studies of the ocean floor. The sequence of rocks dredged from the deep-sea floor (or postulated from geophysical evidence) was found to be remarkably similar to the rock sequence of ophiolites, both in the eastern Mediterranean region studied by Steinmann and in myriad other mountain regions around the globe. Comparisons were first made with "complete" ophiolites, which consist of an uppermost layer of pillow basalts, followed by a sheeted dike complex, a gabbroic complex (similar in composition to the basaltic dikes above, but with a markedly coarser-grained texture), and then an ultramafic complex—usually dunites, peridotites, and serpentinites. Some "complete" ophiolites include: the Troodos massif on the island of Cyprus (considered the best-known ophiolite complex in the world, it includes the serpentine peak of Mount Olympus, where the ancient Greeks quarried steatite for imperial seals, and where today, a number of serpentine endemics grow); the Semail ophiolite in the sultanate of Oman on the Arabian peninsula (the largest in the world, its dark-colored mafic and ultramafic rocks make it clearly identifiable on images from LANDSATs orbiting 570 miles overhead); and the Papuan ophiolite of New Guinea, where, at between 5 and 10 degrees south latitude and with over 80 inches of rainfall annually, a tropical brand of serpentine endemics has been evolving since the Middle Tertiary.

These large, relatively undeformed ophiolites are outnumbered by ophiolites that are incomplete, dismembered, and/or metamorphically deformed. In most cases, the process of obduction, rather than simply and gracefully emplacing the pieces of oceanic crust, has made a mess of the allochthonous mass, spreading parts of it over a

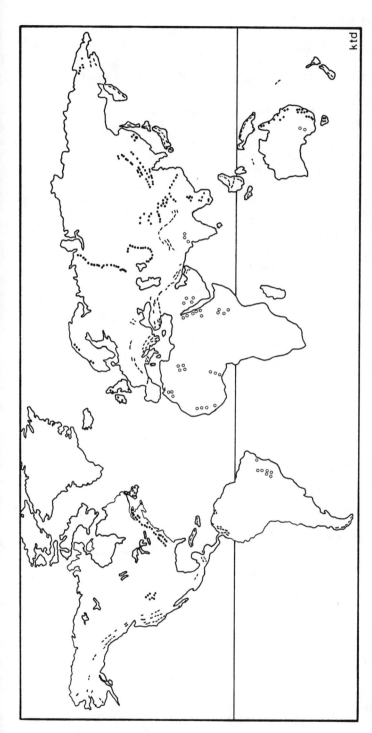

MAP 4   Worldwide ophiolite distribution. Dashed lines represent ophiolites less than 200 million years old. Dots represent ophiolites between 200 and 540 million years old. The open circles represent ophiolites between 540 and 1.2 billion years old. The younger ophiolites are those related to the present cycle of plate tectonics, and are thus close to the sites where oceanic crust is currently being subducted. The median age ophiolites (running along the Appalachians from Georgia to Newfoundland and continuing into Ireland, Scotland, and Norway) mark the closing of the Iapetus ocean in the Paleozoic. (After Gass, 1982)

ktd

MAP 5 Ultramafic rock deposits in Vermont

large area. This is generally what has happened in the Appalachians, where many of the crustal remnants have been altered almost beyond recognition. The peridotite-serpentinite complex in the State Line region of Pennsylvania and Maryland is flanked by gabbroic rock, but there are no sheeted dikes or pillow lavas to be found in the area. North and south of this, most of what remains of the once-complete ophiolites are talc and serpentine deposits, such as the ones at Rose Hill, Broad Creek, the banks of the Wissahickon, the Ochee Springs Quarry, and Florida, Massachusetts.

In northern Vermont (*see Map 5*) and in the Eastern Townships of Quebec there are preserved some larger slices of ocean crust. They were saved from complete destruction by virtue of being located at the "Quebec Reentrant," one of the major reentrants along the Appalachian orogen. The reentrants are approximately marked by the indentations in the present coastline of North America—they alternate with "promontories" that jut out toward the Atlantic. (A quick look at any map of North America will illustrate this crude geometry.) When the North American and Eurasian plates collided, it was the promontories that really took the beating, their rocks being more severely deformed than those at the reentrants.

What do the ultramafic rocks of the Quebec Reentrant tell geologists? They tell of the mechanics of plate interaction during the closing of an ocean, and so geologists make frequent pilgrimages to dunite outcrops in this area. There they map contacts and take samples, and so the more exposed the rock, the better. Vegetation is generally an obstacle to a geologist, hiding his subject rather than revealing it. Follow a group of geologists through the woods; they home in on the outcrops, oblivious to any greenery between them and their rock.

Freestone and Footwarmers

About the same time as Henry D. Rogers was synthesizing his theory of mountain building from his fieldwork in Pennsylvania, there were four geologists homing in on outcrops in Vermont, with similar hopes of unlocking the mysteries of their part of the Appalachian orogen—the Green Mountains. These men—Edward Hitchcock, who had been professor of chemistry and natural history at Amherst College from 1825 to 1845, and more recently served as its president; his assistant, Albert D. Hager; and his two sons, Edward, Jr., professor of hygiene and physical culture at Amherst, and Charles, state geologist of Maine—made up the latest incarnation of the Vermont Geological Survey. The survey had been authorized by the legislature in 1844, but had suffered setback after setback. The first state geologist, Charles B. Adams, after four years of collecting specimens and issuing ineffectual interim reports, wandered off and died while collecting mollusks in St. Thomas. His successor died before publishing the results of his research, and the third state geologist was too feeble to even make his way into the field. In the winter of 1857, shortly after the Vermont General Assembly hired Edward Hitchcock to resuscitate the survey, a fire destroyed the existing geological collection. There were perhaps fifty specimens in the state cabinet to represent thirteen years of rock hounding.

All three of his predecessors had died before the completion of the survey, so Hitchcock took on the task with a considerable feeling of superstition and dread. But providence counseled the Congregationalist minister that despite his own ill health he should recommence the job of investigating Vermont's geologic history. Since Vermont's geological formations ran north and south, his plan was to make east-to-west sections across the state at intervals of a few miles, in order to fix the limits of the various geological formations, determine the strike and dip of the strata, and make a collection of specimens. As it turned out, only thirteen such sections were made; Part Five of the *Report on the Geology of Vermont* (1861), the two-volume final report of the survey, gives their description with no interpretation. Said Charles Hitchcock in his introduction: "We present the facts without any theories. . . . We prefer, at present, to keep within, rather than overstep the bounds of the truth. We do not wish to state anything which the progress of science will show to have been premature."

Hitchcock suggested that the best way to read the "Notes on the Sections" part of the report was to go to the cabinet at the state-house in Montpelier, where were housed the specimens and paintings of the sections, and sequentially digest them, from Section I at floor level on up the wall to Section XIII. Section II, which commenced on the east side of the Connecticut River opposite Brattleboro and extended to the state line at Bennington, was the first traverse to bring the geologists up against outcrops of ultramafic rock, which were indeed the state's southernmost deposits. In Marlboro, the line ran past the Methodist church, just north of which was Hosea Ballou's bed of steatite; a little farther north of this were beds on Ward Belus's and Clark Worden's farms. In the *Report*, no explanations or even questions were posed, just the strike and dip of the rock. The relations of the rock were plain for all to see at the cabinet: the specimens—fist-sized pieces of steatite and chlorite, labeled numbers 38 through 44 on the second shelf—were part of the "talcose schist" formation that ran as a gray watercolor swath down the center of the state. This was ample understanding for the citizens who visited the cabinet; they were much more interested in the fossil beluga whale and mammoth tusks exhibited in glass cases across the room.

Not a single section the survey members made missed some encounter with ultramafic rock. Section III ran across a large bed of steatite and serpentine in Newfane, which was then being worked by the Vermont Marble and Soapstone Company. Section IV led the geologists up a high hill to the Smith and Goodrich steatite quarries in Grafton, which had been worked longer than any others in the state. Beginning in the 1820s, the quarry furnished stone for window caps and sills, fireplaces, pipes for aqueducts, and other uses. When the Hitchcocks visited, 400 tons of stone per year were being extracted. These and a half dozen other locations lay a short walk from the Saxtons River, a major tributary of the Connecticut. The shards of soapstone bowls found at Late Archaic habitation sites in the Connecticut Valley may have been quarried here. Section v, running from the eastern foot of Mount Ascutney to Wells in the western part of the state, again traversed ultramafic rock in Ludlow, where the serpentine had been quarried for verde-antique.

Continuing northward, Section vi struck soapstone at Bridgewater, on the land of George H. Bugbee, a stone's throw from a branch of the Ottauquechee River. Stone from the quarry and mill that once operated there can still be seen in many of the old brick buildings of Woodstock and Bridgewater. Some residents still know the hill nearby the forgotten quarry as "Freestone Hill"; "freestone" is a traditional name for soapstone, deriving from the ease with which it was cut. Section vii met steatite in Bethel, on the land of Peleg Marsh and Rodney Shedd, along the Third Branch of the White River. Albert Hager, forever the hopeful entrepreneur of the survey, speculated that good, workable soapstone could be found on the south side of the river adjacent to the railroad bridge, where it readily could be loaded onto railroad cars with a derrick. It also brought them to William W. Williams's land in Rochester, where he quarried soapstone and sawed it into slabs for use in refrigerators. The association of the soapstone beds with serpentine there were especially apparent, and the geologists spent a considerable amount of time mapping and puzzling over the relations of the two rocks.

Section viii, from Newbury on the Connecticut to the Lake Champlain shore at Bridport, found serpentine high in the mountains at Roxbury. There the American Verde-Antique Marble Company owned a quarry that among its many exports had produced ornamental building stone for the Capitol in Washington, D.C., and the pedestal for a statue of Benjamin Franklin in Boston. It was abandoned in 1858 due to a financial panic, and Hager lamented that there was not greater demand for the stone. Had the Hitchcocks and Hager had a botanist with them, they would have seen that the quarry walls were being colonized by an interesting suite of plants. Section ix brought them to Barnes' Hill in Waterbury, which eighty years after the Hitchcocks' visit would be riddled with mines, but which today bears few traces of the former industry. Section x traversed soapstone and serpentine in Duxbury, Section xi in Johnson, Section xii in Lowell, and the northernmost section, number xiii, traversed Vermont's northernmost ultramafics. In Troy the geologists found two "great ranges" of serpentine and steatite, one on either side of the "Missisco" (Missisquoi) River. Charles Hitchcock wagered nothing about their origin other than to say that Charles Adams, the conchologist who served as the first state geologist, believed that the two ranges defined a synclinal basin, with the steatite mostly beneath the serpentine.

Elsewhere in the *Report on the Geology of Vermont,* there was plenty of speculation about the origin and significance of Vermont's ultramafic rocks. Edward Hitchcock introduced them early on, under the introductory section titled "General Principles of Geology." General principles not only served the lay reader of the report, but served the author by assuring him that despite the great uncertainty surrounding so much of his science, there *were* a few certainties as well. There were certainties like, in Hitchcock's words: "It is not mere hypothesis, but legitimate theory, which leads geologists, with almost no exception, to the belief that the interior of the earth is now in a molten state"; "The new races [of plants and animals] have been introduced not by the gradual change of one species into another, but by the creation of new and successive groups. The earth has changed its inhabitants entirely five or six times"; "Metamorphism furnishes the most plausible theory of the origin of the azoic stratified rocks, which are mica, talc . . . schists, gneiss, serpentine, . . . etc."

Hitchcock introduces serpentine and steatite by saying that they come under the general denomination of "Ophiolites . . . essentially hydrous silicates of magnesia." He saw serpentine, talc, steatite, and chlorite as so nearly identical in chemical constitution that they easily passed into one another. But in pondering their origin, he invokes a greater name than his own, that of Sir William E. Logan, the director of the Geological Survey of Canada, who believed that the abundant ultramafic rocks of Vermont originated as silicious magnesites and dolomites. Hitchcock speculated that other minerals and rocks—garnet, olivine, chondrodite, gabbro, and others—might be capable of producing serpentine by metamorphosis; and concluded by stating that since it is one of the final products of mineral alteration, serpentine is one of the most permanent of rocks. The explanation of its origin was far from permanent, however.

In Vermont, Hitchcock and his associates had found serpentine and steatite principally among the "Azoic" rocks, more specifically as part of what they called the "talcose schist" formation. Despite this association, they knew there was "scarcely any more affinity between steatite and talcose schist than between it and mica schist or gneiss" since the ultramafic rocks always seemed to occur as discrete inclusions in the surrounding rock. Sparked by the situation of the rocks at the Goodrich quarry in Grafton, Charles Hitchcock put forth the possible scenarios for the origin of the puzzling rock: "As the lenticular masses of steatite and serpentine are common, it is no wonder that it is a question with many how these beds were originally derived: whether from aqueous or igneous, or aqueo-igneous forces—or could they have been pockets in the rock which were filled up by chemical deposition?" To get at its chemical and mineralogical character, the Hitchcocks had help from Dr. A. A. Hayes, state assayer of Massachusetts; Dr. C. T. Jackson, of the Boston Society of Natural History; and T. S. Hunt, of the Geological Survey of Canada—all of whom made mineralogical analyses of Vermont ultramafic rocks. They conjured an impressive array of figures of just what percentage water, magnesia, silica, iron, nickel, and other constituents made up the serpentine from Roxbury and Proctorsville. Yet the numbers could not be translated into a theory of origin.

Another avenue to understanding was to compare the Vermont rocks to those of Europe. The verde-antique of Roxbury and Europe were found to be almost identical in chemical composition; still, the Vermont geologists could not accept that the European theory of serpentine genesis—that of intrusion as a molten mass into stratified rock—applied to their deposits. The best they could do was to suggest how the origin could be discerned—by a careful examination of the deposits in each locality. They recognized the serpentine-steatite association ("The connection between serpentine and steatite is seen almost everywhere, and the two rocks often pass insensibly into each other, so that specimens of almost every grade may be found"), but were puzzled by it ("Why the whole mass was not pushed to the ultimate limit of metamorphism, which we suppose to be serpentine, rather than steatite, we confess ourselves unable to show"). Ultimately, they believed that progress in "chemical geology" would provide the answer. They could not have been more wrong.

Albert Hager, the "economical geology" specialist, didn't trouble himself with questions of serpentine's or soapstone's origin, but instead described at great length the merits of the latter material ("it [is] valuable for architectural purposes, and its capability for resisting heat makes it very valuable for lining furnaces, lime kilns, stoves, fireplaces, arches, etc. When reduced to powder it is efficacious in removing grease spots from clothes, by absorption, and in many cases it is advantageously used for lubricating machinery"). Whenever the itinerant geological party came upon an active quarry operation, his enthusiasm for geology grew. He wanted to know the number of men employed, the tons of stone extracted, the horsepower of the steam engines, the nature of export markets, and the names of the managers and owners. About a mile west of Perkinsville, on a tributary of the North Branch of the Black River, Hager came upon quarries operated by the Windham County Mining Company, whose mill produced soapstone posts, window and door caps, and slabs for manufacturing register frames, stove linings, cake griddles, and more. The soft rock found its way into many local homes. In the quarry owner's house were spectacular soapstone mantelpieces; in the workers' houses blocks of steatite were used for many purposes—doorstops, steps, most anything, since they could be had for free. Some of these homes now lie beneath the North Springfield Reservoir. Beyond the dam, there are places on the Black River where you can still find big sawn blocks from the quarry in the riverbed.

Albert Hager, as much as the original people of the Appalachians from the Green Mountains to the Blue Ridge and beyond, was most impressed by soapstone's capacity to withstand intense heat without injury. When Hager visited the Perkinsville quarry, a foreman had placed blocks of soapstone in the fire under the engine boiler, let them become white with heat, and then threw them into cold water. The only apparent change was that they turned slightly yellowish. In *Report on the Geology of Vermont*, there are a far greater number of pages devoted to this type of observation about ultramafic rocks than there are to informed and imaginative theories on their origin. Hager wrote his parts of the report from the comfort of a room heated by a "Stone Franklin" wood stove, manufactured by the Tingley Brothers from the Perkinsville stone. At the conclusion of his ten-page exposition on soapstone, he proudly announced how the stove was "uninjured by crack or blemish." His colleagues' theories about the material would not prove as durable.

With George Henry Perkins, who served as state geologist for the last quarter of the nineteenth century and the first quarter of the twentieth, the scientific questions regarding soapstone's origins were relegated to footwarmer status. Though an able and original observer on a host of scientific problems (he also served for a while as state entomologist and taught botany and zoology at the University of Vermont for sixty-four years, where he initiated the first college course in anthropology in America; in Vermont he was the voice of authority on subjects as diverse as geodes, ancient pottery, tent caterpillars, and the "hygiene of house plants"), Perkins was mainly interested in the relatively unmetamorphosed Paleozoic rocks of the Champlain Basin, and in problems of paleontology and Pleistocene geology. His attention to soapstone and its kindred ultramafic rocks consisted of including photos of the Johnson talc mines or the Roxbury verde-antique quarry and a table of production statistics. He did proudly note in 1917 that Vermont had pulled ahead of New York as the leader in talc production.

While in Hitchcock's day steatite had been quarried in slabs to be turned into a wide range of products—griddles, furnace linings, mantels, laboratory sinks, washtubs, fireless cookers—by the turn of the century its most prominent use was in ground form. Ground soapstone (talc) was used as a white filler in the manufacture of paper; the talc made the paper opaque. In the rubber industry, talc was placed on the surface of molds to prevent material from sticking. It was widely used as an industrial lubricant, to dress hides, in making dynamite, electrical insulating material, and for boiler and steam pipe coverings. Talc was the most common filler in paint, and even illicitly found its way into cheap grades of cotton cloth, whose snow whiteness was obliterated with the first washing, and even into foodstuffs. As to its use as a food adulterant, the 1914 *Annual Report of the State Geologist* stated confidently: "it is the belief of the authorities at Washington that this practice has almost wholly ceased." A more noble use was in soap and talcum powder; though French and Italian talcs were preferred, Green Mountain talc was eventually dusted on some pretty exclusive skins.

By the time Perkins died, in 1933, he had groomed a young man named Eldridge Churchill Jacobs for the position of state geologist. Jacobs had served under Perkins as mineralogist-petrographer (1912–15), field geologist (1916), and then as assistant state geologist (1920); he was a petrologist with a keen interest in igneous phenomena—dikes, vulcanism, and earthquakes—so Vermont's ultramafic "intrusions" fascinated him. His master's thesis at Columbia University (1914) had been on "Talc and Talc Deposits of Vermont," and in it, he had given his untutored opinion as to their origin. He knew from his reading that the serpentine belt of Quebec was considered to be the result of alteration of mafic intrusive rocks such as peridotite. He had also read that the serpentine complexes at Hoboken and Staten Island seemed to be intrusive. But he had seen the Vermont deposits himself, with their array of "grit" (the common name for impure talc), serpentine, talc, and "blackwall" (chlorite-rich rocks typically in a zone between the small, highly deformed Vermont ultramafic bodies and the country rock) and felt a more satisfactory theory was needed. For the time being, he abandoned the old alteration of country rock theory of the Logan-Hitchcock era for one that said the deposits owed their origin to a series of basic (that is, mafic) magmatic intrusions.

Charles Doll, who was state geologist of Vermont from 1947 to 1976, began working with Jacobs in 1927, and under his direction, there was little progress made on the serpentine question, at least in Vermont. The reports issued in the 1950s and 1960s, when they run up against ultramafic rocks, talk about "intrusions," but yield little or no insight as to their origin. The reports failed to consider the fact that most petrologists denied the possibility of the existence of an ultramafic magma. Their laboratory studies showed that the high melting temperatures of certain ultramafic minerals precluded the possibility of a truly liquid ultramafic magma; at best, perhaps the bodies had been crystal "mushes" when intruded.

A few years before Harry Hess published "The History of Ocean Basins" and introduced the concept of sea-floor spreading, he reviewed this situation. The problems of interpretation surrounding serpentine deposits had contributed to what in 1955 Hess termed a "magnificent argument" concerning the existence of liquid ultramafic magmas. "There has been a debate for the past 35 years between the field geologist and the laboratory investigator on how ultramafic rocks are emplaced. The field man has invariably drawn the conclusion that they appear to have been very fluid—liquid—at the time of injection." However, the same field geologists were embarrassed by the lack of contact metamorphism—alteration of the country rock at the contact with the ultramafic bodies—at the sites they studied. The laboratory investigators, meanwhile, repeatedly ruled out each new suggestion as to how such materials could be magmas at a plausible temperature.

Hess had himself proposed a possible scenario for the intrusion of low-temperature alpine-type ultramafic rocks. He suggested that at the onset of orogeny, peridotite in the earth's upper mantle was transformed to a water-rich serpentinite liquid, and that this magma was emplaced in continental crust at low temperatures, where it crystallized as a peridotite or serpentinite. Experimental studies sparked by Hess's suggestion nixed this idea by 1955, but Hess still cast his vote with the field geologist, believing that the field evidence of such an explanation took precedence over discoveries in the laboratory. He had then the nagging feeling that the experimentalists were missing some vital factor.

By 1960 laboratory studies showed that the existence of low-temperature alpine-type ultramafics was possible, leading to an acceptance of Hess's hypothesis of solid intrusion. In the decades following, experiments on the deformation of ultramafic rocks and minerals have further supported that hypothesis, which was the foundation of the North American "ophiolite" hypothesis. In the early 1970s a number of papers advocating the ophiolite explanation appeared almost simultaneously. Steinmann's ideas of a half century earlier, modified by modern petrological and plate tectonics viewpoints, had finally completed their transatlantic crossing. Today, any geologists making "sections" in Vermont (or anywhere in the Appalachians) carry plate tectonic theory as their organizing principle; it is as important to their trade as a rock hammer or Brunton compass. Some of the practical results of the new theory would have pleased Albert Hager; a geologist from the University of Vermont well versed in the ophiolite concept recently discovered in Troy a deposit of talc that may be the largest in the world.

Though Hess made some of his most critical field observations at the Roxbury verde-antique quarry, it wasn't fully considered within the ophiolite framework. Vermont's first ophiolite was Belvidere Mountain, the 3,353-foot peak that contains the largest known reserves of asbestos in the eastern United States. It was this deposit, and its strategic significance, that led to its geologic explication; three U.S. Geological Survey geologists—Alfred H. Chidester, Wallace M. Cady, and Arden L. Albee—carried out work there between 1951 and 1960. In their early reports, they adhered to the conventional theories for the origin of the ultramafic deposits at Belvidere and elsewhere in Vermont, but they eventually became dissatisfied with these. In 1978 the three men published a full report on the rocks of Belvidere and attempted to synthesize a history of sedimentation, volcanic activity, and emplacement of the ultramafic rocks there. The model they presented tried to reconcile the mode of origin of the ultramafic rocks with the concept of sea-floor spreading, and was presented as a general explanation for all the Appalachian ultramafics, not just those at Belvidere.

In their model, a sinuous belt of mantle upwelling that now marks the site of the Appalachian orogen began in the late Precambrian. This belt was 200 to 500 miles northwest of the line along which Africa and North America would later, in the Mesozoic, began to separate. At that time, though, there was one continent, and the floor of the incipient Appalachian eugeosyncline was thick sialic crust. When a rift developed beneath the crust, caused by the outward movement of upper mantle rocks, it was distended and downwarped. The Appalachian eugeosyncline was born. The rift continued, and sediments poured into the deepening eugeosyncline. At the same time, basaltic lava erupted into the eugeosyncline as sills, surface flows, and volcanic piles, but were continually reduced by erosion. This explained why the volcanic activity showed up as detrital volcanic beds within the Appalachian eugeosynclinal sedimentary sequence, rather than as discrete pillow lava or sheeted dike sequences flanking the ultramafic rocks, as they did in Steinmann's classic model.

As peridotite in the upper mantel swelled toward the crust, it cooled and became hydrated; in essence it was partly serpentinized. Serpentinization continued as the bodies of ultramafic rock were kneaded upward into wet sediments. Large bodies, such as Belvidere, contained large masses of unaltered dunite in their centers, whereas smaller bodies, such as the dozens in Vermont that sported talc and soapstone quarries, were completely serpentinized. It was then, hundreds of millions of years ago, that the stage was set for where canoe-wanderers would go for potstone and where plant evolution would take on new serpentine twists.

Funeral Dress
of Kings

**Belvidere (literally, and ironically, "beautiful view") Mountain
is at the uppermost end of the Missisquoi River in northern**
Vermont. The Abenaki Indians, whose last stronghold in Vermont
was at the mouth of the river, called it Wázowategók, which freely
translates to "at the river which turns back." This refers to the
changeable course of the 117-mile-long stream; it first runs north by
east across the Canadian border, then turns southwest, and finally
makes two sharp bends before flowing into Lake Champlain. On
Belvidere, however, all this fluvial doubling and redoubling is far
away. A half dozen mountain streams make their way off the south
and east flanks of the 3,360-foot peak and head north to join other
streams that drain the area of the Upper Missisquoi Valley. Some of
these streams have strange beginnings, originating as gullies that
follow the fall line of 200-foot-high tailings piles of crushed serpentine and dunite. From the Green Mountain Ridge 40 miles to
the south, the piles are clearly visible, as strange, greenish-gray
mountains bare of vegetation. Up close, they are almost equally bare,
dotted only by a few small aspens and gray birches, struggling black-
berry canes, and an occasional wild strawberry, dandelion, and
patch of hairgrass. Despite the lack of vegetation, the surface of the
piles presents a hundred shades of green in the quarter-size chips of
crushed rock.

   The 30-million-ton piles of stone are the product of Belvidere
Mountain's vast open-pit asbestos mines. The asbestos-bearing rock
deposits, which cover about 3,000 acres on the mountain, were
known to geologists as early as 1859, when they were examined by
Charles H. Hitchcock and his brother Edward as they traversed one
of the sections for the Vermont Geological Survey. They pointed out
in *Report on the Geology of Vermont* that asbestos fibers as fine as

flax were found around Belvidere "in considerable quantity, lying loosely in the soil." At that time, asbestos knew only a few uses, perhaps most frequently as a lining in fireproof "salamander" safes. The term *salamander* for this and other articles impervious to flame came by way of the ancient Greek notion that the cold-skinned creatures had the power to endure fire without harm. Though the Roman naturalist Pliny the Elder later debunked this superstition by unceremoniously tossing a salamander into a fire and burning it to a crisp, Greek science was less sophisticated and asbestos came to be regarded as "salamander wool." The filmy white fibers found in the rock on Mount Olympus were thought to be pieces of salamander hide that had rubbed off.

The Greeks also gave us the word *asbestos*, meaning inextinguishable. They made use of the mineral's magic properties, weaving the fiber into cerecloths for kings and noblemen. In Rome, where the strange stuff was called "amiantus"—undefiled, pure, incorruptible—asbestos continued to be the province of royalty, spun into perpetual wicks for the sacred lamps of the vestal virgins and the table linen of the emperor, who delighted in cleaning his asbestos napkin by tossing it in the fire and withdrawing it whiter than before. During the Dark Ages, the use of asbestos in Europe declined, but it still figured in a historical incident smacking of myth. The Emperor Charlemagne, threatened with invasion by a rival kingdom, called a peace conference and pulled a bit of prestidigitation, throwing an asbestos tablecloth into the fire. When the king of the Franks drew it out and exhibited it unharmed, the enemy ambassadors returned to their ruler with reports of Charlemagne's magical powers, and war was averted. After a long hiatus, asbestos's properties were rediscovered and adapted to the new machines of the Industrial Revolution; it was used widely to insulate boilers, steam pipes, turbines, ovens, and kilns, and there were even experiments with producing incombustible clothing.

America's appetite for raw materials was growing apace in the late nineteenth century, and the state geological surveys such as the one the Hitchcock brothers were engaged in were meant to find new sources for that appetite. But the true "discovery" of asbestos at Belvidere Mountain was no scientific endeavor; it came on the serendipitous wings of accident. In 1948 Ned Hinds, who spent his ninety-three years 2 miles from the asbestos mines in the village of Eden Mills, told the story of the discovery to Edna Beel Engle, a summer resident of the town, who transcribed it as follows:

Oh, I can't rightly say what date it wa-a-s. But the mills was still runnin' so I know it was before 1900. . . .

I was workin' in the sawmill—foot o' the mountain. There was a man up in Canada, name o' Kuchie—or some such—who owned 600 acres up on Belvidere Mountain. He sent down a man, name o' Tucker, with a crew of Frenchmen to timber it. When the snow was on the ground, they'd work till 'twas hard to see and then the logs was drawed down on bobsleds. Them heavy logs on a bobsled made a wonderful smooth track. Why! 'twas like glass. Some of the woodsmen would wait till the logs was down and then they'd come down on that track ridin' on shovels. . . . Yessir. They'd sit on the blade of a shovel with the handle out in front to steer with. And they could come from the top o' the mountain to the camp at the bottom in two-three minutes. Traveled like lightnin'! . . .

One day, just afore dark, a log sled broke off a piece o' rock over to the side and it rolled onto the track. The first Frenchie to come down on a shovel hit that stun and it knocked him galley west. . . . Wa-a-l, he picked hisself up and looked to see what caused the accident. The rock was about as big as a peck measure, so he put it on the blade and drawed it on down to camp.

That night, after supper, some of us was settin' round in the baaroom over to the hotel when this fella came in. "I had a shipwreck today . . . and it was caused by this funny lookin' piece o' rock."

Tucker comes into the baa-room while we was examinin' it and he said he never seen nothin' like it before. He took his pen knife and scraped out some of this fuzzy stuff. . . .

He was a cunnin' ole fox, that Tucker. Next mornin' he takes that stun into the shop and hammers it into pieces and sends one o' them pieces to Washington. Sure enough, the word comes back from Washin'ton that it was purely asbestos and very valuable.

Wa-a-l, the news traveled. Some folks, who owned the property alongside, come up from Massachusetts to start minin' as-

bestos from their land. They ruined quite a few people sellin'
em stock to buy the machinery to dig it out.

Residents of Lowell and Eden today tell a similar story, lacking the
detail that old Ned provided, but confirming the approximate date
and principal characters. Some versions give the credit for identification, as well as discovery, of the valuable mineral to an anonymous
French-Canadian logger, who knew the white fibrous substance as
"l'amiante" or "pierre à cotton" from seeing it in the serpentine hills
of Black Lake and Thetford in Quebec's Eastern Townships. Who-
ever discovered it, it was Melvin E. Tucker who exploited the discovery first, prospecting a few miles along the belt of asbestos-bearing
ultramafic rock before ultimately opening a quarry on the northeast
side of the mountain. Within two years, half a dozen other groups
joined him, these backed up by entrepreneurs in southern New
England. There were the New England Milling and Mining Company of Fall River, Massachusetts, the National Mining and Development Company on the south side, and the Vermont Asbestos
Company, which opened a ledge northeast of Tucker's quarry. Other
companies that bought mining rights and began work at Belvidere
included the United States Asbestos Company and the Lamoille Asbestos Company. None of these companies got very far, however.
After laboriously digging out the asbestos veins by hand, they didn't
have the proper machines for refining it. Teams of horses drawing
out ore would get mired in mud. The New England Milling and Mining Company even built a mill for grinding the stone to extract the
fiber, but failed to establish markets for its material, and thousands
of bags of asbestos stood around and rotted. The company finally
sold some of it to local people, who used it in place of sand for plas-
tering their walls.

In 1921 exploitation of the Belvidere deposit moved from cottage
industry to capitalist enterprise. The Asbestos Corporation of America incorporated in Boston and sought to raise a million dollars in
gold bonds to back up their mining venture. The capital bought
steam-driven tramways, boom derricks, cable hoists, rotary crush-
ers, and conveyor belts to Belvidere. Only a decade before, asbestos
production had been a largely machineless affair. In Russia, mines
in the Ural Mountains and Mongolia, owned by barons and counts,
had had a feudal labor structure. As many as seventeen hundred

Russian muzhiks, or peasants, were recruited each year from the surrounding farm villages, and they were paid about thirty-five cents a day. During harvest, the mines ground to a halt as the men returned to their crops. In Mongolia, the mine owners had even greater difficulty, being dependent on a nomadic tribe—the Buriats—for mine workers. These people, "not industrious nor very intelligent" in the eyes of the entrepreneurs, were more content to roam the country herding cattle than to work in the asbestos mines.

At Belvidere, a new form of peasantry was employed. Some of the peasants were local folk who saw no future in farming and to whom migration to larger Vermont towns such as Saint Albans or Newport was too harrowing an adventure. Such migration was not uncommon; the population of Eden, which peaked at nearly 1,000 people in 1870, was only 738 in 1900, and had declined by another couple of hundred by 1930. Today the town's population is only about 650, while neighboring Lowell in the 1980 census had 580 inhabitants, and Eden boasted a little more than 200.

With such a small population from which to draw, the mine owners went beyond the Upper Missisquoi hinterland for their labor force. Italian quarry workers from the Barre granite region were recruited, and a huge boardinghouse was built to house the "Eye-talians," as locals called them. The dormitory was part of an enormous complex that incorporated offices, the manager's residence, storerooms and stockrooms, and a laundry. Mrs. Lloyd Dolan, who lived there as a child while her father managed the mill, remembers how tremendous the place seemed; there were stone washtubs in the laundry, pretty green shades over the big desks in the office, a dumbwaiter to bring food to the workers' mess hall on the second floor, and hot running water in their part of the house. There was even a dynamo to generate electricity, and a spectacular glass widow's walk that looked off over the as yet undefiled landscape. You could see the "Eye-talian" schoolhouse from there, and Tillotson's sawmill, which processed the huge volume of timber that was stripped from the mountain to get at the asbestos. Mrs. Dolan remembers looking off from the widow's walk during the 1927 flood, marveling at the water above the tops of the remaining trees.

Presiding over all this was an unlikely figure, a "widda-woman" from Philadelphia named Mrs. Gallagher who'd ended up with a controlling interest in the stock of the Asbestos Corporation of America. The company's efforts at abstraction had been foundering, so she and her brother William came to Vermont to run the mine. She was frail and elderly, relying on a female companion to help her about while she surveyed the enterprise from her shiny '27 roadster or the widow's walk. Her brother, meanwhile, did his best to make the mine a paying proposition; he lobbied for a railroad spur to be built from Newport so that the asbestos fiber could be sent cheaply to distant markets. He kept the accounts, talked to geologists, fretted over the fluctuating price of raw asbestos—but all to no avail. By 1929 the Gallaghers had poured their entire fortune into the deepening hole in Belvidere's side, and they went bankrupt. Mrs. Dolan's last and most vivid memory of that era was of Mrs. Gallagher standing on the big porch of the boardinghouse crying because she'd just notice that the sawmill, which had always been clearly visible, wasn't part of the landscape anymore. Mrs. Dolan was only six then, but she knew that she wasn't supposed to tell the fragile woman the obvious truth, that the mill had burned years before. It was one more symbol of ruination, of decay, and it seemed to break her spirit. The Gallaghers retreated to Philadelphia, and the big house stood empty. Mrs. Dolan remembers the many times her father had to chase away people who'd come to loot plumbing fixtures or furniture.

From the ashes of the Asbestos Corporation of America rose the Vermont Asbestos Corporation, but their balance sheet never looked much better than Mrs. Gallagher's, and in 1936 they sold their land, buildings, and equipment to the Ruberoid Company, a leading producer of asbestos building materials. After extensive exploration to determine the extent of economically available ore, Ruberoid opened a quarry downslope and east of the Eden quarry and built a new mill. By the mid-1940s, the Belvidere mines were producing over 90 percent of all United States asbestos. But while the asbestos industry grew, and with it the tailings piles at Belvidere, something else was growing. It was an uneasiness, a sense that the undefiled white mineral had a dark side.

As early as 1900 a doctor at Charing Cross Hospital in London had made the first autopsy description of pulmonary fibrosis—lung cancer—in an asbestos worker. In 1902 asbestos was included by the inspector of factories in the list of dusts known to be injurious. In the next two decades only a few articles about asbestosis were published each year, but not all of them were in obscure medical journals. In 1903 two articles appeared in the widely read *Scientific American*. In 1913 the first states enacted workmen's compensation statutes that covered asbestosis. By the time the big boardinghouse was built for the Belvidere mine workers, the number of publications about asbestosis had mushroomed. Perhaps the Barre granite workers saw work at the asbestos mines as the lesser of two evils, for silicosis rates among granite cutters ran at about 50 percent. Miners' consumption, stonecutters' asthma, stonemasons' disease, grinders' rot—no matter what it was called, silicosis was an established fact among granite workers, while its analog among asbestos laborers—asbestosis—was only on the verge of recognition.

In 1935 the Metropolitan Life Insurance Company published a three-year study of Canadian and Atlantic seaboard asbestos mines and mills, which had been done at the request of officials of the Johns-Manville Company (then fast becoming the world's largest asbestos corporation). From over a hundred X-ray examinations the doctor who conducted the study, Anthony J. Lanza, concluded that prolonged exposure to asbestos could cause pulmonary fibrosis and recommended that industry seriously face the problem of dust control in asbestos plants. Dr. Lanza became a leading figure in the field of occupational medicine, and as he did so he was slowly but surely bought by the asbestos industry. In 1938, in his book *Asbestosis and Silicosis,* Lanza declared that damage suits against the industry "confused and terrified industrialists and insurance officials" and inspired "dread" among them. Lanza knew whereof he spoke, because by that time Johns-Manville and Raybestos-Manhattan were already being sued by workers with asbestosis; in 1933 they had settled eleven such suits for $35,000. At that time they also bought the plaintiff's lawyer, who agreed not to bring any more lawsuits. Thirty-five years later, when the first of tens of thousands of men who were dying from the cumulative effects of occupational exposure to asbestos began renewed suits against Manville and other industry companies, the lawyers for the defense would deny they had ever known about the dangers of asbestos.

Old-timers in Lowell and Eden tell of the days when the whole mountain was white with dust, and those that worked in the mines tell stories about working without respirators in areas where the dust was so thick you couldn't see more than five feet away. Such conditions can't exist today; government agencies such as the Environmental Protection Agency (EPA) and the Occupational Safety and Health Administration (OSHA) see to this. Or do they? Visit the Belvidere quarries today and stop at the front office. Everything—

desks, windowsills, chairs, idle hard hats—is covered with a fine white dust. Talk to the management and mine workers, who see government inspectors as a nuisance and brag of the days working in the asbestos mill when they couldn't see the man working next to them. If you are interested in the history of the Belvidere mines, the plant manager will give you a little handout answering your questions. The last page is a question-and-answer sheet called "Asbestos and Health," answering such questions as "Can a little bit of asbestos kill you?" "Should asbestos be banned until proven safe?" "What is industry doing about the problem?" The answers are all predictably favorable toward industry, since the sheet is a publication of the North American asbestos industry's trade association, the Asbestos Information Association (AIA), which is sponsored by GAF, Johns-Manville, Raybestos-Manhattan, and others.

The Xerox sheet says that the industry began studying asbestos-related diseases in the late 1920s and used the information to begin dust-control programs, which cost "tens of millions of dollars." The industry also was currently "sponsoring or co-operating in major epidemiological and other research projects designed to identify and eliminate asbestos-related health risks within the industry, and also for fabricators and applicators of finished asbestos-containing products." The truth of the matter is that the asbestos industry has consistently denied that asbestos can and does kill people, and for over a half century has done everything it can to avoid responsibility for the deaths of its workers. One New Jersey court, in declaring that the largest of the asbestos companies—Manville (formerly Johns-Manville)—had withheld information about the asbestos hazard from workers since the 1930s, said Manville "made a conscious, cold-blooded business decision, in utter flagrant disregard of the rights of others, to take no protective or remedial action."

Initially, workers' compensation statutes acted as the principle barrier to workers' seeking recompense for asbestos-related disease, but this barrier eventually gave way. Since 1970 there have been tens of thousands of suits filed by asbestos workers against their employers, but none ever came from workers at the Belvidere quarry. Though they acknowledge that "asbestos is a dirty word," current and former mine workers maintain the asbestos is safe. They were always told that it was the California or South Africa asbestos that was harmful, not their Belvidere fibers, and they believed it. Though they'll admit to knowing co-workers who died of lung cancer, they quickly add that they were heavy cigarette smokers. One can't help feeling that the paucity of lawsuits around Belvidere is due more to the fact that the nearest lawyer is 10 miles away than to safe working conditions at the mine.

The lawsuits and the long-overdue regulation of the workplace put a strain on the asbestos industry, and in 1974 GAF announced its intention to close the mine because of an EPA mandate to invest a million dollars in antipollution equipment. The company claimed it wasn't worth spending so much money on a mine that was almost depleted. The maintenance supervisor of the mine, a Canadian named John Lupien, and a few other employees got the idea that the workers should buy the mine and keep it open. Instead of looking for other jobs, Lupien and 177 other mine workers set out to raise enough money to buy the mine and run it themselves. By March 1975 they had raised $100,000, persuaded the state of Vermont to guarantee $1.5 million in bank loans, and got GAF to take a note for another part of the final $2 million dollar price tag. As the Vermont Asbestos Group, the workers bought the mine, becoming the largest employee-owned operation in the United States. Everything began going their way. An unexpected asbestos shortage caused prices to rise 30 percent. The Defense Department made huge orders for asbestos. Efficiency rose sharply. At the end of a year, the worker-owned company had made $1 million dollars on $7 million in sales. Pension benefits were boosted by 50 percent, a $15 quarterly dividend on the $50 shares was paid, and workers got a 72-cent hike in their hourly wage. A processing plant was built in nearby Morrisville to make decorative fire-retardant wall paneling. Just as the plant was finished, asbestos prices fell dramatically. The processing plant serves as a warehouse now, storing the hundred-pound bags of raw asbestos fiber that will go overseas, mostly to Third World countries. Both workers and management at the mine speak of asbestos's heyday as something permanently past.

The discovery of Vermont's first serpentinophyte, unlike the discovery of asbestos, came by design rather than by accident, but it came from the same slope as the one that yielded the fibrous rock. Having collected the Aleutian maidenhair fern, *Adiantum pedatum* var. *aleuticum*, from Mount Orford in Quebec, and knowing that Belvidere was "in the same range and of the same asbestos formation," an amateur named L. Frances Jolley explored Belvidere for the rare fern. She found it on a hot day in July 1922, growing in crevices of rock in full sunshine. The differences in form of the serpentine variety and the typical maidenhair fern are striking: typical maidenhair's most distinctive character is its fan-shaped, horizontally spreading pinnae (the term for the leaflets of a "once-cut" fern leaf), whereas the serpentine variety's leaflets point upward; the pinnules (or sub-leaflets) are oblong on the typical variety of maidenhair and have rounded ends, whereas the serpentine plants' pinnules are wing-shaped and have pointed ends.

All these distinctions were clear to Jolley; others were not. When she guided fellow plant hunters from the Vermont Botanical and Bird Club to the site later that summer, they neatly classified their understanding of the rare fern: variety *aleuticum* grew in the open, on asbestos-bearing rock; the common maidenhair grew in moist, shady soil. There were no more questions to ask, except perhaps whether it grew anywhere else in the state. But no one took up that question. Whether for lack of adequate geological maps or disinterest, the scores of other ultramafic outcrops of the Upper Missisquoi Valley went unbotanized. Vermont's cadre of amateur botanists were guided by their mentor, Cyrus G. Pringle, who once said: "quit the broad place of dull sameness, seek out every possible situation of exceptional character, and look to find amidst peculiar conditions rare and localized plants." The generation of plant hunters that followed Pringle heeded his advice; they combed quartzite ridgetops, alpine summits, limy headlands on Lake Champlain, sphagnum bogs, sand plains, and cedar swamps. Not one, however, hunted outcrops of serpentine. The archipelago of ultramafic rock running down the spine of the Green Mountains awaited botanical discovery.

It wasn't for lack of good botanists, but for lack of botanists who saw rocks as well as plants. In 1899 Willard Eggleston, who went on to a distinguished botanical career with the U.S. Department of Agriculture, discovered the large-leaved sandwort, *Arenaria macrophylla*, on what Eggleston took to be "limestone ledges" in Proctorsville. It was the first New England station reported for the plant. A few years later, S. J. Ballard reported the plant from "coarse, pebbly soil" in Newfane. Back at the Proctorsville site a year later, Eggleston found a curious raspberry bush growing out of crevices in the same rock. The leaves of the anomalous raspberry were small, rounded, and only rarely were they divided into threes, like those of the common raspberry. Eggleston sent the puzzling raspberry to M. L. Fernald at Harvard, who pronounced it identical to a variety known from northern Europe—*Rubus idaeus* var. *anomalous*. Though it was more glandular than the European shrub (a "serpentinomorphic" trait), Fernald thought the reversion to round leaves—a distinctly "primitive" characteristic—to be diagnostic. Had Eggleston correctly identified the habitat of the anomalous raspberry—serpentine—Fernald may have thought differently about the plant. Though "Eggleston's raspberry" (its current name is *Rubus idaeus* var. *Egglestoni*) was later found about 20 miles south on another ultramafic deposit, that collector again misidentified the rock, and no connection to serpentine was made.

It wasn't until 1958 that a second plant was positively tied to an ultramafic substrate. Phil Cook, a recent graduate of the University of Vermont, was driving east from Montgomery to Lowell through Hazen's Notch with his brother, a geologist, when they spied an outcrop near the top of Haystack Mountain. Cook was interested in alpine plants and thought the outcrop might sport some interesting alpine species, so they hiked the Long Trail south to the Haystack Ridge, periodically shimmying up trees to pinpoint their target outcrop. Though the bedrock geology of the region had recently been mapped by U.S. Geological Survey geologists, it hadn't yet been published, so the brothers were unaware of what rock they might find there. The botanist of the pair was also completely unaware of the botanical effects of ultramafic rock. What they found delighted them both; the botanist got his alpine plants, and the geologist got to explore Vermont's highest ultramafic outcrop. Had he not been along, the substrate's identity may have again gone unnoticed. Though only at an elevation of 3,200 feet, the north-facing cliffs harbored a suite of arctic and alpine plants: arctic black crowberry (*Empetrum nigrum*); alpine bentgrass (*Agrostis borealis*); alpine bilberry (*Vaccinium uliginosum* var. *alpinum*); northern tufted bulrush (*Scirpus caespitosus* var. *callosus*); and mountain clubmoss (*Lycopodium selago*). The crowberry and bentgrass were known from two other places in Vermont—the treeless summits of Camel's Hump and Mount Mansfield, Vermont's two highest mountains, where these plants grew at elevations 1,000 and 800 feet higher, respectively, than on Haystack's dunite knob. It was a clear case of the "elevational displacement" aspect of the serpentine syndrome.

The most spectacular find at Haystack was not these rare plants, but an even rarer one. *Arenaria marcescens*, the marcescent sandwort, had never been found in the United States, its nearest station being Mont Albert on the Gaspé Peninsula. Its name comes from the fact that, like some other members of its serpentine-loving family, the Caryophyllaceae, it lays prostrate upon mats of the previous year's dead ("marcescent") foliage. This habit seems to reinforce the feeling that the plant is rooted here, in the harsh edaphic environment, unable to colonize nearby nonultramafic substrates. It suggests antiquity also, the layers of brown leaves and old carpels saying that even herbs have histories. When it greens out from below these strata, it announces tenacity more than the goldthread and bunchberry growing below the stunted balsam fir and red spruce of the summit do.

It's an ungentle place, that dunite knob. Visit on a hot day in May, and you'll find snow lying in hollows between the ledges. Summer almost never arrives there; the knob is locked in a perennial Pleistocene past. Juncos and white-throated sparrows are the only animal companions there; familiar creatures but boreal to the bone. Standing on the gray-green rock and looking north, you can just make out the glacier receding northward, leaving this and other ultramafic islands isolated, an ocean of coniferous and deciduous forest in between. In May green shoots of the bulrush and hairgrass (*Deschampsia flexuosa*) probe up out of dead, scruffy tufts, and only the little basal leaves of a ubiquitous serpentinophyte—the harebell, *Campanula rotundifolia*—are visible. It's a hard place to know, this dunite knob, dropping almost vertically 20 to 30 feet to a little plateau below. A botanist couldn't count stems to get a clear estimate of the entire United States population of *Arenaria marcescens*, unless he came in by helicopter. Even then it would be difficult.

After trying to negotiate the wet dunite cliffs, you resign yourself to surveying them from the base. At its eastern edge, the cliff assumes strange shapes in the dying evening light. The joints in the rock become runes, and the gray lichens are petroglyphs. Pits in the wall turn into claw marks, and you can make out a series of skeletal faces staring out at you. The faces have voices. They tell you that you are back at Bald Friar on the Susquehanna, at the steatite blocks on the Wissahickon. Somehow the strange green rock has taken a place in your mind as primal as a snake.

Some similarity, real or imagined, ties the serpentine spots together, but there is difference too. The Haystack Mountain serpentine community shares only two herbaceous species—*Deschampsia flexuosa* and *Campanula rotundifolia*—with the ultramafic outcrops of the rest of the Upper Missisquoi Valley. These outcrops, generally below 2,000 feet in elevation, have few trees, usually white pine, white birch, red maple, and red spruce. Below them grow a fairly fixed group of shrubs—velvetleaf blueberry (*Vaccinium myrtilloides*), wild raisin (*Viburnum cassinoides*), meadowsweet (*Spiraea latifolia*), and juniper (*Juniperus communis*). The herbs on these outcrops include, in decreasing abundance, bracken (*Pteridium aquilinum*), common polypody (*Polypodium virginianum*), early saxifrage (*Saxifraga virginiensis*), tufted hairgrass (*Deschampsia flexuosa*), mouse-ear chickweed (*Cerastium arvense*), maidenhair spleenwort (*Asplenium trichomanes*), harebell (*Campanula rotundifolia*), rock sandwort (*Arenaria stricta*), and yarrow (*Achillea millefolium*).

The two plants that could be said to be serpentine "indicators" on these outcrops are *Arenaria macrophylla* and *Adiantum pedatum* var. *aleuticum*. In the Upper Missisquoi Valley, they occur wherever dunite crops out from below the soil. There is no spectacular serpentine effect as in California or even the State Line barrens. In the glaciated Vermont terrain, the forests on ultramafic rock look pretty similar to those off it. It isn't for lack of rock; there are over a hundred ultramafic deposits in Vermont, from North Jay Peak, a mile and a half south of "Journey's End," where the Long Trail meets the Canadian border, to Halifax, Vermont, which borders Massachusetts. They range in size from the East Dover deposit—four and a half miles long and slightly less than a mile wide—to ultramafic pods and lenses a few hundred yards in area. Though it is less than 3 degrees latitudinally from the Upper Missisquoi Valley deposits, the East Dover deposit harbors an entirely different suite of plants. This body, which is mostly dunite, and is well exposed, being cut diagonally by the Rock River and three of its tributaries, is overlain by a forest of no real distinction. Red maple, hemlock, red spruce, and white pine are the predominant trees, with an understory of witch hazel, juniper, and other shrubs. In the middle of the deposit grows a colony of another shrub, mountain laurel (*Kalmia latifolia*). Mountain laurel is uncommon in Vermont, restricted largely to the lower Connecticut and West River valleys, where it is at its northern range limit. The handsome, shiny-leaved shrub is a Hypsithermal relic there, surviving in the relatively more moderate microclimates of a few southern Vermont river valleys. But the East Dover colony is no protected spot; its presence there seems another example of serpentine's "latitudinal displacement" effect, this time providing conditions for the northward displacement of a more southern plant.

Conspicuously absent from the ledges of the East Dover deposit are the typical Upper Missisquoi ultramafic associates—harebell, early saxifrage, rock sandwort, mouse-ear chickweed, and maidenhair spleenwort—but the large-leaved sandwort spreads along the crevices in some places where the dunite shows itself. Farther north, at Proctorsville, *Arenaria macrophylla* is more vigorous, usually growing in lightly shaded or fully exposed dunite or serpentine ledges, cliffs, or talus. Though it occasionally grows under the full shade of a forest canopy, the plant reproduces there mainly by runners, flowering infrequently. Walking uphill across the deposit, the ultramafic ledges take on an increasingly "Upper Missisquoi" feel as you near the summit. Harebell and chickweed are conspicuous wherever *Arenaria macrophylla* grows, as is maidenhair spleenwort. Continuing up, little "balds" covered by *Arenaria macrophylla, Asplenium trichomanes*, and *Campanula rotundifolia* appear, along with a new serpentine indicator—*Selaginella rupestris*, rock spikemoss. The truly "northern" serpentine plant—*Adiantum pedatum* var. *aleuticum*—is still absent, however.

Between Proctorsville and Belvidere, Vermont's ultramafic outcrops remain largely unexplored, except at Roxbury, where the old verde-antique quarry provides plenty of exposed rock for serpentinophytes. Looking down from the top of the quarry, it's obvious that wherever plants can get a hold, they are serpentine lovers. The three-inch-wide ledges between successive vertical rocksaw cuts are covered with *Saxifraga virginiensis, Arenaria macrophylla, Selaginella rupestris, Asplenium trichomanes*, and a few other species. Though the Aleutian maidenhair fern doesn't survive there, two other fern rarities—rusty woodsia (*Woodsia ilvensis*) and male fern (*Dryopteris filix-mas*)—do.

The understanding of serpentine plants in Vermont (and the rest of New England) is in 1987 at about the same place as the understanding of more thoroughly studied serpentine vegetation complexes (such as the State Line or the "western"—California, Oregon, and Washington—barrens) were half a century ago. The study of

New England's ultramafic vegetation is still at a floristic level; it aims at enumeration of what grows where, straining when larger questions of why and how are posed . . .

. . . Except for one botanist working on one species, the maidenhair fern. Though ferns are generally a puzzling group taxonomically, *Adiantum* is one of its most clearly circumscribed genera, and the *Adiantum pedatum* "complex," the northernmost element of the largely tropical New World group, is equally well described. That description adequately limits the complex, but fails when it comes to describing variation *within*. The most recent major pteridophyte (fern) flora of North America recognizes four subspecies in the complex: *Adiantum pedatum* subspecies *pedatum*, the common, universally admired fern of the eastern deciduous woods; subspecies *calderi*, a name recently given by William J. Cody to plants limited to serpentine outcrops in both the Appalachian and western North America mountain belts; subspecies *aleuticum* of the western cordillera; and subspecies *subpumilum*, a dwarf fern limited to a few stations on coastal cliffs in the Pacific Northwest. (Thus far, I have been calling the serpentine variety *Adiantum pedatum* var. *aleuticum*.)

When Cody proposed his new subspecies, *Adiantum pedatum* ssp. *calderi*, in 1983, he did so using traditional taxonomic methods. Both *calderi* and *aleuticum*, by his key, separated out from *A. p. pedatum* by virtue of their strongly ascending branches, and *calderi* was distinguished from the more northern *aleuticum* subspecies by its more tightly clumped fronds, its glaucous, little-incised pinnules, and its conspicuous indusia (the protective membrane covering the spore-containing fruitdots). These are obvious differences, even to the untrained eye, but evolution is not something that one can always see with the eye. In proposing his new classification, Cody looked at some three hundred specimens collected by Pehr Kalm in Virginia in 1749. Surely this, along with tramping the deciduous woodlands around Ottawa, where he lives, was enough to give Cody a firm Gestalt for the classic, archetypal maidenhair fern. He also looked at over a hundred sheets of subspecies *aleuticum*, including L. F. Jolley's Belvidere plants, Fernald's Mont Albert plants, Marie-Victorin's Coleraine, Black Lake, and Thetford plants, and even plants from the serpentine tableland at Bonne Bay, Newfoundland. He collected maidenhair ferns from ultramafic area in Washington State, looked at California specimens, traveled to the cold ravine on Mont Albert where Fernald first got what he took to be *aleuticum* in 1905. Through all this looking, Cody had only one question in mind: is there enough morphological variation to give subspecific status to the serpentine group of maidenhair?

When Cathy Paris tackled the maidenhair, she of course had the classification dilemma as one of her questions, but it was perhaps the least important. Her primary question was whether there was a genetic basis to the variation observed in *Adiantum pedatum*. Second, she wished to know how this variation was compartmentalized, that is, at what level—population versus individual—it occurred. An ancillary question was the role that serpentine soils played in this variation. Finally, she wanted to discern the stable characters of the plants by which the true genetic relationship could be established. Her methods, though not new, had never been tried on any serpentine endemic in eastern North America.

Paris's work began with gathering plant material to study. Whereas Linnaeus, Fernald, even Cody, to some extent, relied heavily on more than just their own collections to build their various taxonomies, Paris collected all of her material herself. During the summers of 1983 through 1985 she collected *Adiantum pedatum* from twelve populations on nonserpentine soils—nine in Vermont and one each from Wisconsin, Nebraska, and Kansas—and eight serpentine populations. Most of the serpentine ferns came from outcrops of the Upper Missisquoi Valley—Belvidere, Brown's Ledges, Mineral Springs Knob, a road cut along Route 58 in Lowell—but she also collected at Mont Albert on Quebec's Gaspé Peninsula and at White Cap Mountain in western Maine, where there were a few small, extremely isolated ultramafic outcrops that managed to sport some serpentine plants. At each of these sites, she gathered leaves, rhizomes (roots), spores, and at least one living sporophyte that she could bring back to a laboratory garden (called a "common garden") at the University of Vermont. In addition to her work at these eastern North American populations, she traveled west to collect serpentine and nonserpentine representatives of *Adiantum* in Washington and Idaho. Using living plants, Paris first set out to determine which characters, especially of those commonly employed in plant keys and taxonomic diagnoses such as Cody's, were stable and which were susceptible to environmental modification. From a preliminary group of fifty-six plants, which included fourteen plants each from an eastern and western serpentine and nonserpentine population, she selected thirty-six characters for study. About half of these were pinnule (the ultimate segment of the fern leaf) characters—length, width, breadth of incisions, and the like.

In a sense what distinguished this beginning level of analysis— the morphometric, that is, the "shape" of the plants—from what others had done was the size of Paris's sample. Linnaeus and Fernald stored incredible amounts of information mainly in their heads. Even they would have been taxed by the two thousand-plus measurements generated by Paris's study. She fed the data into a computer and came up with a group of sixteen characters that were considered useful for future statistical analyses. The greenhouse experiments also demonstrated that certain characters were "environmental"— for example, the color and degree of twisting of the pinnules was determined by the amount of exposure to light the plants had, while others—such as the size and texture of the leaves—were substrate (soil) dependent. At the grossest level, the stable characters seemed to be that nonserpentine plants had rounded pinnules and divisions in the upper margin, whereas serpentine plants did not. Also, the lower midrib of the serpentine ferns was at an acute angle to the rachis (stem), whereas in nonserpentine plants this midrib was perpendicular.

Along with the morphometric investigation, Paris used the technique of gel electrophoresis to get at her question of whether variation in *Adiantum* had a genetic basis. In electrophoresis, pieces of fresh tissue (in this case immature *Adiantum* leaves) are ground in a liquid buffering solution, absorbed onto wicks of chromatography paper, and then exposed to a weak electric field. Individual amino acids that make up the proteins of the plant tissue may have a positive, negative, or neutral charge. Genetic change that causes the substitution of one amino acid for another may change the total charge of the protein molecule, so that it moves quite differently in an electric field.

What Paris found could never have been anticipated by Linnaeus, Fernald, or Cody. She found that the *Adiantum pedatum* complex in eastern North America was composed of three distinct genetic entities: a diploid fern of rich woodlands, a diploid of serpentine substrates, and a tetraploid fern also restricted to serpentine, which she presumed to have been derived from a hybrid between the two diploids. "Diploid" and "tetraploid" refer to the number of chromosomes in the somatic (body) cells of the ferns; the tetraploid fern has twice the number of chromosomes as its diploid progenitors. Polyploidy, from the Greek words *poly* (many) and *ploos* (fold), is the condition by which genetic isolation is produced without geographic isolation and is not uncommon among ferns. Because the two serpentine populations are impinged upon by the same set of environmental variables, their leaf structure varying in response to exposure and soil moisture, the two groups are easily confused. Via electrophoresis, however, Paris showed that there was more to serpentine maidenhair fern than met the eye.

The importance of Paris's work is that it gives us a better understanding of the evolutionary history of the maidenhair fern. Her genetic studies suggested that the serpentine tetraploid from the Upper Missisquoi region is a "neopolyploid"—that is, recently derived taxon, a new "critter" in evolutionary terms. A number of attributes of the tetraploid maidenhair suggest this. Like other typical neopolyploids, the Upper Missisquoi region tetraploid ferns show duplicated gene loci; over time, there is a tendency for such nonessential duplications to be lost. The other line of evidence is a more traditional one—its limited distribution. In polyploid species, geographic range is often a function of age, thus "old" polyploids commonly exceed the range of their diploid progenitors. "Young" polyploids, however, have quite limited ranges relative to their parent diploids, whose ranges usually overlap. The distribution of maidenhair fern in eastern North America suggests a young polyploid complex, since the two diploids, within the edaphic restrictions peculiar to them, are wide-ranging and they occur in close proximity. The tetraploid fern, by contrast, is limited to a few stations, and these stations are within the range of its progenitors.

In her effort to explain the origin of the serpentine maidenhair fern, Paris drew upon a body of theory and methodology rooted most directly in two places—the theories of endemism of G. Ledyard Stebbins and the experimental work of Arthur R. Kruckeberg. In 1942 Stebbins published a paper titled "The Genetic Approach to Problems of Rare and Endemic Species," in which he proposed that there are two types of endemics: "depleted" and "insular." The depleted endemics, which were old but not necessarily senescent (that is, declining), had acquired endemic status through the gradual loss of their "biotypes," the range of variants within a population. These biotypes had formerly allowed the species to exploit a great variety of habitats. By the process of "biotype depletion," some species had been pared down to a single or just a few biotypes specifically adapted to a localized or specialized habitat. The other type of endemic, the insular species (which did not necessarily, as its name would suggest, live on an island), could have originated from a few isolated individuals preadapted to a specific habitat. Stebbins's theories were inspired to a great extent by the patterns of speciation he'd observed on California serpentines.

Arthur Kruckeberg was a student of Stebbins who had absorbed Stebbins's genetic approach and had also been bitten by the serpentine bug. After looking at serpentine vegetation in northern California, he had three main questions: (1) Why were so many plant species excluded from serpentine soils? (2) Why were some species able to grow successfully on serpentine? (3) Why were some species restricted to serpentine soils? Kruckeberg's hypothesis was that, as shown by a number of previous studies, the capacity of serpentine plants to grow on soils of low calcium levels was a critical limiting factor. For certain species occuring both on and off serpentine, Kruckeberg expected to find populations within the species adapted to these low levels and others not so adapted.

To test his hypothesis, Kruckeberg in the 1950s carried out experiments on plants classified as "bodenvag" and "bodenstets" according to the terminology of German botanist F. Unger. Bodenvags (German for "soil wandering") are wide-ranging species of plants that occur both on and off serpentine, whereas bodenstets are restricted by a requirement for a specific chemical substance in the soil of serpentine. He collected seeds of a number of bodenvag species from both serpentine and nonserpentine sites, and then grew the seeds on nonserpentine and on serpentine soil amended by different levels of calcium. Although the degree of response differed, a surprisingly large number (twelve of twenty-one studied) of the bodenvag species displayed differentiation into serpentine and nonserpentine races. In pursuing this course of research, Kruckeberg took his lead from a group of Carnegie Institution of Washington botanists (based at Stanford University) who had demonstrated the existence of chains of more or less discrete, climatically adapted *ecotypes* in a number of perennial species ranging from sea level to above timberline in California. Their studies showed that though the same species, a yarrow from the Sierra Nevada just would not grow on the Tiburon Peninsula. Kruckeberg found that serpentine soil had just as selective an effect on populations within a wide-ranging (bodenvag) species as did climate.

When Cathy Paris began her work on *Adiantum pedatum*, she had never heard of bodenvags and bodenstets. She hadn't studied under a serpentine fanatic. As a new graduate student on a fall field trip, maidenhair was one of the few ferns that she recognized. The leader of that trip, who later became her thesis adviser (and ultimately, her husband), mentioned that there was an interesting variety of the fern that grew on serpentine. She had an interest in geology and thought the "serpentine problem" as it applied to maidenhair might make a good research topic. Why had it taken so long for anyone to investigate? Her impression was that the question had been kicking around for a long time—as casual comments between pteridologists and occasionally as a question mark of sorts in regional floras—but that because serpentine was uncommon, and the plant even more uncommon, the problem was less compelling than other fern enigmas.

Paris remained interested enough in the serpentine maidenhair problem to continue her investigation as a doctoral dissertation. Her model of maidenhair evolution has it originating in eastern Asia, migrating to western North America, and finally via serpentine to the eastern part of North America. In her opinion, the plants on serpentine in the east are more closely related to western North American plants than to their congeners growing in nearby deciduous woods. Indeed, it could well be that the maidenhair fern of the eastern North America woodland is the most recently derived taxon; the specimens that Pehr Kalm collected and Linnaeus first described may be the "weird" ones. As with the scientific questions of aboriginal steatite use and the origin of the Appalachian ultramafics, the questions asked and the observations made by scientists today may be the same as those of a century ago. The difference is in the information on hand to make interpretations.

Mont Albert and the Nunatak Debate

The largest ultramafic deposit of the Quebec Reentrant is Mont Albert on the Gaspé Peninsula (*see Map 6*). **A large serpentine** tableland, Mont Albert appears to the unbotanically minded visitor to be essentially destitute of vegetation. Dr. A. P. Low, the director of the Geological Survey of Canada, described the area in 1884:

> The top of Mont Albert is nearly flat, and is rent by a deep gorge on the east side, which, near its head, splits into several smaller ones. The sides of these gorges are quite destitute of vegetation and the bare serpentine rocks are weathered to a light buff color. On the top of the mountain blocks of serpentine are scattered around, and are partially covered by a thick growth of mosses and lichens. Sheltered places are occupied by a stunted growth of black spruce, which rarely attains a height of ten feet. The branches interlace near the ground and form an inpenetrable thicket. The whole surface has a dead appearance, and reminds one of the pictures of the moon.

To the botanist, Mont Albert is hardly so lifeless, but is rather a "roofless Noah's ark" (as Frère Marie-Victorin called it) preserving a host of "preglacial" plants. At the turn of the century, however, the flora of Mont Albert was unknown, this ultramafic outpost being for North American botanists something like what the entire Gaspé had been for others—the "end of the earth." (This is the translation of the word *Gespeg*, the Micmac Indians' name for the peninsula. *Gespeg* became *Gachepé* to Champlain when he arrived in the early seventeenth century. Whether "surface of the moon" or "end of the earth," Mont Albert was a blank spot on the botanical map until 1905, when Merritt Lyndon Fernald visited the area.)

Fernald, who would later become the foremost authority on the flora of the northeastern United States and adjacent Canada, was then an assistant professor of botany at Harvard. Along with J. Franklin Collins, a botanist from Brown University, Fernald botanized his way up the limestone sea cliffs of the northern Gaspé coast, until he reached the village of Sainte Anne des Monts. From there the botanists headed inland, led by a well-known guide and hunter, Sam Coté.

Unlike the geologist A. P. Low, Fernald and Collins found on this tableland, supposedly "destitute of vegetation," a wealth of extremely interesting plants. Tucked among the angular serpentine boulders and frost-shattered scree were a host of plants that were either completely unknown or known only from very distant regions. Out on the naked tableland and along the icy streams that dissect its flanks, Fernald and Collins found a peculiar fern covering hundreds of acres—*Adiantum pedatum* var. *aleuticum*. They found two other "western" ferns—*Pellaea densa* and *Polystichum mohroides* var. *scopulinum*. *Pellaea densa* (called by some taxonomists *Cheilanthes siliquosa*), commonly known as Oregon cliffbrake, is a wiry fern with rigid, triangular fronds and is found on dry, rocky slopes. It is characteristic of the Sierra Nevada of California and the Cascade and Coast ranges northward into southern British Columbia, its station farthest east prior to its discovery at Mont Albert having been at three single Rocky Mountain stations in Montana, Wyoming, and Utah. *Polystichum mohroides* var. *scopulinum* was equally foreign, being mostly confined to arid regions of the Sierra Nevada–Cascade axis with a few isolated stations in the Tetons, the Wasatch, and the Mission Mountains.

These ferns were not the only surprises. They found two grasses of the western cordillera—*Festuca scabrella* and *Danthonia intermedia*—both of which have 1,500-mile range disjunctions. The same was true of *Salix brachycarpa*, a beautiful little willow with silky-white foliage and tiny catkins, found by Fernald on Mont Albert but known before 1905 only from the mountains and high plains of eastern British Columbia, Washington, and Oregon eastward to Saskatchewan, Montana, Wyoming, and Colorado. A couple of other prostrate willows known from the West were also found by Fernald and Collins.

Along with the western disjuncts, Fernald and Collins found plants of the far north—the arctic sandworts, *Arenaria marcescens*, *A.*

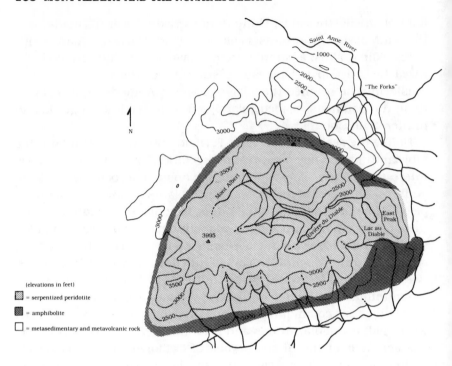

MAP 6   Mont Albert and environs

humifusa and *A. sajanensis;* the alpine campion, *Lychnis alpina* var. *americana;* and the only arctic goldenrod, *Solidago multi-radiata*. Though pestered by *les sacrées mouches* (their French-Canadian guides' term for black flies), Fernald and Collins were thrilled by their discoveries. As soon as they would stop to collect one novelty, another would divert them. Fernald and Collins found on Mont Albert a situation similar to that on the serpentine barrens of the central Appalachians—the ultramafic substrate formed a distinct vegetational discontinuity in the landscape. There in the Gaspé, instead of a transition from a luxuriant hardwood forest to a pitch pine-scrub oak parkland, they found a nearly straight line dividing the *Salix-Adiantum-Arenaria* barrens on serpentine from the Hud-

sonian "puckerbrush" forest that occurred on the surrounding am-
phibolite rock. For Fernald, the contrast between the floras of the
two substrates was so vivid that he was stimulated to a new line of
research.

Although all natural scientists are schooled in journal keeping
early in their training, it is the collecting botanist who is usually the
most compulsive diarist. Fernald was no exception. His account of
botanical trips on the Gaspé and in Newfoundland, culled from his
journals and published in *Rhodora,* the journal of the New England
Botanical Club, paint a detailed and lively portrait of the life of a field
botanist around the turn of the century.

Fernald had made his first wilderness botanical expedition with
"Frank" Collins in 1892, when Collins invited Fernald to join him for
several days of camping, fishing, and botanizing along the Kennebec
and Dead rivers in northern Maine. Collins, ten years Fernald's
senior, quickly became Fernald's friend and perennial traveling companion, rather than mentor. In Fernald's 1942 reminiscence of field-
work with Collins, he was "quiet, undemonstrative, of few words,
sensitively sympathetic, always with a quiet, dry humor, a master of
woodcraft, mechanical technique, and specimen-making . . . for 32
years it was a very exceptional summer which did not find us exploring or camping or botanizing somewhere in New England or the
Gaspé Peninsula."

One way that Collins did serve as mentor was as a model diarist.
He never failed to make an entry at the end of a day of botanical exploration, no matter how adverse the conditions. The entries differ
markedly from Fernald's own style in that they are dry factual accounts, with no "frills." The logistical details of the first Mont Albert
expedition are laid out plainly in Collins's diary:

August 6, 1905, Sunday. Cloudy and hazy. Spent all day on
river, going from Marten River Camp to Main Camp, a short
distance below the Forks. Hard poling.

August 7, 1905, Monday. Rain last night and most of the day.
Toasted driers before fire and fixed up camp to protect against
rain. Coté caught some trout and shot two ducks. Breakfast of
potatoes, coffee, etc. Dinner of trout, duck, tomatoes, etc.

August 8, 1905, Tuesday. Clearing somewhat last evening
and cooler. Broke camp about 9:00 AM. Fernald and I carried
small packs, cameras, and collecting boxes. We went up over a

nearby ridge and then down through a ravine, then up the mountain, stopping every ten minutes for a rest. Coté, the two Gagnon boys, and Joe Fortin carried heavy packs. We reached an altitude of 3250 feet about 1:30 PM and decided to camp there. Coté, Fernald, and I stayed on the mountain; the rest of the men went down to the river-camp. About 3 PM Fernald and I went higher up the mountain, botanizing, and left Coté to fix camp. He came up the mountain later. We found the nearest peak (East Peak) about 3650 feet high, and a still higher peak to the west-northwest. To the south of these there is an immense tableland sloping gently to the southward. The eastern end of this tableland is a great serpentine rock barren, and western a bog or meadow. To the south is a deep gorge with three large snow-banks in view. Beyond this is the main (highest) part of the mountain—a still larger desolate-looking rock-barren plateau sloping gently to the main dome. We found extremely interesting plants—many of them unknown to Fernald.

Fernald inherited Collins's diaries upon his death, and when he published some of them in *Rhodora*, he punctuated them with comments more typical of his own journal keeping. Where Collins noted that the two botanists "decided to go in a barge" to Sainte Anne des Monts, the starting point for trips into the Shickshocks, since no one would haul their trunks over the rough mountain roads, Fernald interjects that the craft was a "lobster-boat with decayed fish smearing the whole inside." Where Collins notes that they boarded at "Ed LeFrançois' place," Fernald lists the menu: "'bifstek,' carrots, baked potatoes, lettuce, graham bread, a choice of 23 kinds of relish and condiments . . . pickled beets, cake, and cherries!" On the last day at Mont Albert, Collins begins his entry: "Got up about 3:30 AM on account of cold." Fernald comments: "I well remember the greeting from Coté, in characteristic Canadian French, as I crawled out of the tent. 'Fer fret cum job' ('Il fait froid comme le Diable')."

The following summer, Collins and Fernald returned to the Mont Albert region, hiring Coté and Fortin again as guides. The morning that they set out upriver a disgruntled woodsman whom Fernald playfully called "Zéphirin Violette" met them at the trail head, yelling wildly in French that they had made a terrible mistake. Coté knew nothing about the woods, he shouted, and insisted they employ him instead. The botanists knew better. On that trip, while Collins and

Fernald went wild collecting on Mont Albert, Coté blazed a trail to the granitic Tabletop Mountain (now Mont Jacques-Cartier), which Fernald was keen on visiting, particularly because he wished to see how its acidophilous flora contrasted with the basiphilous flora of Mont Albert. Despite being savagely bitten by insects, Coté managed to find his way to the mountain and back, having located an old overgrown trail. The next day, when Coté led the botanists, Fernald recognized the fading blaze marks as those of the geologist who'd found Mont Albert so lifeless—A. P. Low.

Woodcraft was not the guides' only skill. According to Fernald, Joe Fortin became an able botanical assistant, catching on to the Latin names of the plants and identifying difficult species. Once, when the two men split up to explore either side of a pond, Fernald called across to Fortin, "Is there anything new over there, Joe?" and got the immediate reply, "No, there's nothing here but *Subularia aquatica* and *Isoëtes macrospora.*" For Fortin and Coté, though, the real reward of their backcountry expeditions with the American botanists was the rich harvest of game, not plants. They caught good-size trout by the dozens and killed the abundant "savons" (spruce grouse) by pitching stones at them. The birds were essentially tame, having had little or no contact with humans. The greatest prize for Sam Coté was the opportunity to scout the moose hunting for autumn. Though Fernald does not mention them, they probably also saw caribou; today a herd of about 250 caribou, as disjunct as many of the serpentine plants, survives on the tundra of Mont Albert and Mont Jacques-Cartier.

In 1907 Fernald considered its serpentine-endemic plants of Mont Albert, along with a variety of other arctic, alpine, and subalpine floras, in a paper titled "Soil Preferences of Certain Alpine and Subalpine Plants." He pointed out how the comparatively meager flora of the serpentine tableland was extremely rich in plants unknown elsewhere south of the Saint Lawrence River—by his count there were at least twenty-one such plants, but the number might be as high as forty, since the taxonomic identity of some was at the time still in doubt. Though fascinated by this observation, he proposed no grand explanatory schemes, simply dwelling on the significance of geology and soil chemistry to the distribution of alpine plants.

The island of Newfoundland, across the Gulf of Saint Lawrence from the Gaspé, was another botanical unknown, and beginning in 1910 Fernald led a series of expeditions to the island to fill a void in the botanical knowledge of the region. There at the northern terminus of the Appalachians, in the Long Range, lay the other bits of exhumed ocean crust that Fernald was eager to explore. The largest was Table Mountain, where Fernald and student assistant Joseph Kittredge, Jr., made, in the words of Fernald,

> a first attack upon the serpentine barren which, five miles west of Birchy Cove, forms the northeastern flank of the Blomidon (with some propriety corrupted to "Blow-me-down") Range. We went with keen anticipations, for this serpentine barren from a distance looks so like a reduced Mt. Albert that we felt it inevitable that it should yield the plants which in the Gaspé distinguish the serpentine from all the other mountains. And we were in no way disappointed. Here was Mt. Albert all over again; and during the whole summer we did not have a closer day's work than on that single day in late July when, starting soon after sunrise, we tramped in to the mountain from Benoit's Cove in a heavy thunderstorm which rendered more obscure an overgrown trail, climbed up to the tableland botanizing all the way, came down over a snow-field at the risk of our lives as it proved, thus teaching us a valuable lesson in mountaineering, and returned before dark five miles through the woods to Benoit's Cove. Our boxes and ruck-sacks were crowded full and Mt. Albert, the great serpentine tableland, will be suggested in the plants we had found.

What plants had they found? *Adiantum pedatum* var. *aleuticum* and the other western ferns, the two grasses *Festuca scabrella* and *Danthonia intermedia, Lychnis alpina americana, Arenaria humifusa* and *A. marcescens* were all there along with most of Mont Albert's other rarities. Besides being important additions to Newfoundland's flora, the occurrence of these species on Table Mountain sparked a new hypothesis in Fernald's mind. A grander theme than the one of soil preferences of alpine plants began to shape itself, and the plants of the serpentine tablelands of Mont Albert and Table Mountain were essential to this theme. Writing in 1918, Fernald said: "it is the relic species now localized in isolated areas which give us clues to the long cycles of plant migrations—marches and countermarches—which have accompanied the different geological epochs since the early Cretaceous; and it is to these relic colonies, both of plants and animals, that the historical geologist must turn in the reconstruction of ancient lands now quite obliterated or buried beneath the great oceans."

Seven years later the theme that was evolving in Fernald's mind emerged full blown in a 1925 paper titled "The Persistence of Plants in Unglaciated Areas of Boreal America." By drawing on a mixture of evidence from the fields of plant geography, plant ecology, geology, and population genetics, Fernald sought to explain the disrupted ranges and special habitats of the rare serpentine plants of Mont Albert and Table Mountain with the hypothesis that they had survived the Pleistocene isolated on nunatak refugia, small islands of land surrounded by the ice fields of the Pleistocene ice sheets. This "nunatak theory," as it came to be called, was Fernald's attempt to explain the relict floras (the disjunct and endemic Cordilleran and arctic plants) of the Shickshocks and the Long Range, and a number of other areas centered around the Gulf of Saint Lawrence.

What evidence did Fernald present in support of the nunatak theory? First, there was the botanical evidence—the mixture of arctic and southern taxa on the broad plateau uplands of the Shickshocks and Long Range suggested to him that these areas served as refugia during the Pleistocene. In addition, Fernald listed some 296 western "relicts" and endemics with disjunct distributions for these same areas. This botanical evidence seemed to coincide with the observations and interpretations of Canadian geologists such as R. Bell (1863), R. Chalmers (1905), A. P. Coleman (1919), and F. J. Alcock (1921) that these very same spots escaped glaciation. They cited such evidence as the absence of erratic boulders above 2,500 feet in the Shickshocks and 500–1,000 feet on Table Mountain in Newfoundland, the lack of glacial striations on bedrock and roches moutonnées in these areas, and the lack of a widespread or deep mantle of boulder clay. The felsenmeer—deep, rotted, angular residual soils—that these geologists found on the uplands were considered by them to be evidence of great age, and hence of the lack of glacial scouring.

To account for the failure of the relict species to spread from these limited areas despite some eleven thousand years of ice freedom, Fernald hypothesized that the severe stresses of glaciation had allowed only a few biotypes (those plants sharing the same genetic makeup) to find suitable ecological niches in which to wait out the "big freeze." Later, when the climate ameliorated, these survivors did not have the genetic diversity needed to expand into the rich mosaic of new niches left in the wake of the retreating ice. Fernald also believed the plants in question to be "senescent" species, that is, ones that were too old and conservative to pioneer in new habitats. To illustrate this point Fernald contrasted the nunatak flora with that of the Coastal Plain flora of Nova Scotia, which he characterized as young, aggressive, and pioneering. The prevailing assumption among botanists of the day was that the age of a species was reflected in how clearly marked it was, and the nunatak species were certainly more thoroughly differentiated from their congeners than were the endemics of the Coastal Plain flora.

The interest in the idea of "species age" was at its height around the time Fernald put forth the nunatak theory, and so it is no surprise that the concept of "species senescence" looms large in Fernald's theory. As with most botanists and plant geographers of the early twentieth century, Fernald's thoughts on the issue of species age had been stimulated by J. C. Willis's "age and area hypothesis" (1922). The hypothesis simply stated that the size of a species range was proportionate to its age. In Willis's mind the hypothesis meant that small ranges were associated with species of recent origin, whereas larger, more cosmopolitan geographic ranges signified older species. Willis was working with the stable floras of tropical Africa and Asia though, and botanists working in temperate and cold climates were quick to point out that many taxa with restricted ranges were relics of formerly extensive distribution. Fernald was perhaps the most prominent of Willis's critics, and in 1923 at the Botanical Society of America's Age and Area Hypothesis Symposium, he garnered his Newfoundland and Gaspé data not only to refute Willis's hypothesis, but essentially to reverse it, at least as it was applied to biota of higher latitudes. Fernald's data showed the "ancient" floras to be more restricted than the wide-ranging youthful species.

The age and area hypothesis was only one of a variety of concepts and assumptions that helped shape Fernald's nunatak theory. It was the era also of land bridges in zoogeography and phytogeography; the "cycles of erosion" of William Morris Davis in geomorphology; "climax communities" in plant ecology; and among plant taxonomists, a vastly different view from today's of just what constituted a species. In addition, the field of geology, which lent corroborative evidence to Fernald's theory, was barely settling down into its new view of the Quaternary. Finally, eighty years after the publication of

Agassiz's *Études sur les Glaciers* (1840), icebergs and "drifts" were out, and geologists were free to work out the details of movement of a continental ice sheet. Yet despite the existence of a unifying principle, the methods for working out these details were in their infancy. A poignant example of this is that F. J. Alcock, one of the geologists whose observations and opinions Fernald cited as supportive of an ice-free upland area in 1925, had by 1935 changed his mind. He joined a then-growing group of geologists who saw the nunatak theory as unlikely based on the geological evidence.

Botanists, too, began to find fault with Fernald's theory. In 1937 V. C. Wynne-Edwards published findings that merited at least some modifications of the nunatak theory, and a year later Frère Marie-Victorin, the distinguished French-Canadian botanist whose professional career had been initiated with help from Fernald, marshaled additional criticisms of the theory. Marie-Victorin questioned the senescent status of the endemics and proposed as an alternative to the nunatak theory two hypotheses of his own. Wynne-Edwards (1937) used ecological rather than historical arguments to explain the problem of the rare western and arctic taxa in the region. He tied their restriction to their affinity for specific substrates: basiphilous for cordilleran taxa and both acidophilous and basiphilous for arctic ones.

Though Fernald's original paper (1925) deals with a great number of species besides the serpentine endemics, the serpentinophytes figure importantly in the dissenting views of both Marie-Victorin and Wynne-Edwards. Wynne-Edwards (1937) pointed out that the ultramafics outcropped widely in the Eastern Townships of Quebec, and that on these unmistakably glaciated outcrops were found a number of "nunatak" relicts—for example, *Adiantum pedatum* var. *aleuticum*, *Pellaea densa*, and *Festuca scabrella*. Wynne-Edwards argued that the nunatak theory offered little help in explaining the contemporary distribution of species such as these. It is ironic that the locations of the species cited by Wynne-Edwards were in many instances discoveries of Frère Marie-Victorin, who had first gone to Mont Albert in 1923 after Fernald had strongly encouraged him to do so. Familiar with the serpentine flora of Mont Albert, Marie-Victorin had in subsequent years botanized extensively the serpentine "collines" of Mégantic and Wolfe counties, where he and others continued to turn up new stations for the "nunatak" species.

Marie-Victorin's life was strangely intertwined with that of M. L.

Fernald, and with serpentine. Born Conrad Kirouac in April 1885 at Kingsley Falls in the Eastern Townships of Quebec, he was one of eleven children, five of whom died at an early age. His own health was poor; at age eighteen, shortly after he entered the Brothers of Christian Schools, he was diagnosed as having tuberculosis, and his doctor prescribed rest and fresh air. Botany was suggested as a therapeutic hobby. He went into the woods with Abbé Provancher's old flora, *Flore canadienne*, in hand, but he didn't know how to use it. Admiring a trout lily, *Erythronium americanum*, he was puzzled over how to find it in the book, when a peasant walking by told him the French vernacular name—*ail douce* (sweet garlic). He found the name in the book's index, and the logic of the flora—its use of dichotomous keys to identify plants—was revealed to him. He was now Frère Marie-Victorin, botanist.

In 1909 Marie-Victorin began corresponding with Fernald, seeking his authority on plants he collected around Quebec. At that time their correspondence concerned only problems of identification, not evolution and speciation. As late as 1913 the Christian brother Marie-Victorin had published an anti-Darwinian article in Canada's principal professional journal of natural science, *Le Naturaliste canadien*. By the time Fernald had convinced him to visit Mont Albert, Marie-Victorin had been wooed to the theory of evolution by the Jesuit father Teilhard de Chardin.

Marie-Victorin, accompanied by his longtime botanical companion Frère Rolland-Germain, along with three others, got his first view of Mont Albert on August 6, 1923:

> Beautiful day. We left around 9:30 AM for the serpentine region. . . . On the summit and off toward the southwest, we noticed an interesting formation of dried ferns. A little beyond, a plateau bordered by a belt of *Scirpus caespitosus* and diverse *Carex*. We were now in a meadow apparently very poor, but in reality rich in alpine species: *Lychnis alpina, Arenaria sp., Rhododendron lapponicum, Statice sibirica, Solidago sp., Artemisia borealis, Kalmia polifolia, Ledum groenlandicum . . . Andromeda glaucophylla, Silene acaulis*, diverse grasses.
>
> In descending the ravine we came up, we found the first specimens of "l'Adiante aleuticum" (*Adiantum pedatum* variety *aleuticum*), and a little lower, *Pellaea densa* and *Polystichum scopulinum*, a *Solidago* and an *Aster*, and many *Salix*.

We returned for dinner around 2 PM and spent the rest of the afternoon preparing the riches we'd collected.

Subsequent diary entries record the same botanical discoveries made by Fernald and Collins almost two decades earlier, as well as some nonbotanical observations: "lundi, 13 août. Pluie toute la matinée . . . Pluie tout l'après-midi. Découragement, langueur, idées de suicide." Though suicide did not fell Marie-Victorin, his weak constitution did; he suffered a mild heart attack and had to be carried down Mont Albert by his guides.

The following winter Marie-Victorin finally met his botanical correspondent of fifteen years at the Gray Herbarium, where Fernald went over his Mont Albert plants. Fernald knew from a few visits to the Eastern Townships that the line of serpentine hills encompassing the asbestos-producing regions of Thetford, Black Lake, Broughton, and the like, nourished an erratic flora similar to that on Mont Albert. He encouraged Marie-Victorin to explore these areas more thoroughly than he had been able to do.

The nunatak theory was a hotly debated topic in those years, and some botanists who'd worked amicably together for many years parted company over ideological differences. Fernald and Marie-Victorin did not always agree on questions of phytogeography; in December 1931 a rumor was circulating among Marie-Victorin's colleagues that Fernald was attacking Marie-Victorin and his work because of spite over theoretical disputes. Marie-Victorin sent Fernald the following telegram: "Rumor circulated here that you are going to unite with Louis Lalonde to attack my work and Dept. Botany University Montreal. . . . Can hardly believe old friendship aching. If all this humbug please wire collect immediately." That afternoon Marie-Victorin received a telegram from Cambridge: "Rumor groundless. Have no time for petty politics and recriminations. Glad to encourage all good work. M. L. Fernald." After this, Fernald began his letters "Dear Victorin" instead of "Dear Brother Victorin," and Marie-Victorin no longer wrote "Dear Dr. Fernald," but "My Dear Friend."

Marie-Victorin had for some time wished to visit Black Lake, where the pteridologist E. T. Wherry had collected the rare Oregon cliffbrake *Pellaea densa*. On July 15, 1944, Marie-Victorin set out from Montreal with Frère Rolland-Germain and three students. They stopped to botanize at several spots along the way and were successful in finding several colonies of the desired fern. On the way home, the group stopped at the village of Saint Norbert, where Marie-Victorin visited with relatives and called on a childhood friend. About halfway home, a car crashed head-on into the party of botanists. Though the others survived, the shock of the collision was too great for Marie-Victorin's heart, and he died after his friends tried unsuccessfully to revive him.

After Wynne-Edwards and Marie-Victorin, few voices were raised by the botanical community in opposition to the nunatak theory for a number of years, not so much because it was widely believed, but because it ceased to attract the kind of scholarly attention that had made it a "controversial" issue in the 1920s and 1930s. Quietly though, botanical (and geological) evidence refuting Fernald's nunatak theory continued to mount. In the 1950s Olaf Rune, a Swedish botanist who had studied serpentine endemics in his native country, and H. J. Scoggan, a Canadian botanist, made extensive surveys of the Gaspé flora and came to conclusions similar to those of Wynne-Edwards. Along with the importance of the serpentine barrens, they recognized the role of unstable, frost-disturbed soils and steep, cold, wet sea cliffs in the distribution of many of the region's rare plants. Apparently they survived where these special ecological conditions checked competition from the widespread, successful boreal and arctic flora. This same situation seemed to prevail in another locality where some of Fernald's nunatak species, along with other arctic taxa, have been turned up in recent decades—on cold, rocky headlands on Lake Superior. Here again the newer plant ecological view is that the climate does not allow the boreal forest to colonize and replace the northern plants.

Perhaps the most convincing argument against Fernald's theory came in 1969, when W. H. Drury, Jr., in a very evenhanded discussion of the problem of plant persistence in the Gulf of Saint Lawrence area, reexamined Fernald's 1925 plant lists. From Fernald's original list of 406 species and 136 varieties, Drury removed as no longer valid those species that (a) have since been found scattered across the Canadian Shield, that is, Ontario, James Bay, Lake Mistassini, etc.; (b) have since been found in lowland areas of Quebec, New Brunswick, Nova Scotia, and New England; (c) have been recorded from areas flooded by the Champlain Sea; (d) evidence suggests were introduced by humans to Newfoundland.

Because of many changes in taxonomic treatments of the plants on Fernald's 1925 list, it was difficult for Drury to make a completely accurate accounting of the species and varieties. However, the results of his accounting produce a list drastically different from Fernald's: 367 species and 120 varieties were removed, leaving perhaps 45 species and varieties. Of these "allowed" plants, many are specialized halophytes, calciphytes, or serpentinophytes. Others belong to critical genera in which speciation is usually quite rapid. A good example of this is the group of four serpentine endemic willows—*Salix arctica* var. *antiplasta, Salix hebecarpa, Salix brachycarpa,* and *Salix chlorolepis*—that were among the survivors of Drury's cuts. Willows are notoriously plastic, and the characters that differentiate these four species from one another and/or their nonserpentine congeners are fairly obscure ones. In the end, after habitat specialists and critical genera were removed, Drury found fewer than ten species and varieties that conformed to the conditions originally outlined by Fernald as distinguishing true "nunatak" plants, that is, having no other plausible explanation for their disjunct distribution. After Drury's analysis, the nunatak theory had been exhausted of virtually all of its explanatory power. Except to a small circle of true believers, the theory became relegated to the status of an interesting but outdated "thought artifact."

One of the wonderful things about the natural world is that it never yields its data to science all at once, hiding its contradictions, exceptions, and abundant anomalies under a cloak of complexity and change. (Hidden, too, by the presumptions of its investigators. Marie-Victorin, who often mused on philosophical questions in between his discussions of botanical problems, once remarked in his journal: "That is the reason why it is necessary to collect these slices of life that chance gives each day and each hour to the botanist who applies himself to see and integrate the new acquisitions in the frame of the old ones.") Just as textbooks and teachers were getting comfortable with treating the nunatak theory as outmoded, new geological evidence bearing on Fernald's theory has against been unearthed. In 1977 D. R. Grant, of the Geological Survey of Canada, published findings that show there is now better geological corroboration of Fernald's hypothesis of nunatak botanic refugia. According to Grant, evidence from scattered stratigraphic sections and from the relationship of a sequence of ice-flow indicators to a raised interglacial marine platform, together with the limits of freshly glaciated terrain against weathered bedrock areas, indicates that late Wisconsin glaciers spread weakly toward the present coast. These

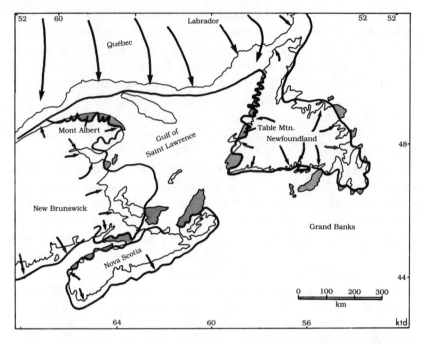

MAP 7   Limit of late Wisconsin glaciers (bold line) in the Gulf of Saint Lawrence region. Nunataks and other extra-glacial areas (shaded) and main directions of ice movement (arrows) are also shown. (After Grant, 1977)

glaciers were fed by a complex of small ice caps located on broad lowlands and uplands, with centripetal flow toward the Gulf of Saint Lawrence. In the process, large areas of land remained unglaciated. Included in Grant's map of unglaciated regions are the serpentine tablelands—Mont Albert in the Gaspé and Table Mountain in the Long Range of Newfoundland (*see Map 7*).

Despite the new evidence, for botanists the task at hand now appears to be working out more of the details of long-range dispersal for these specialized serpentine plants. Whether or not species such as *Arenaria marcescens*, *Pellaea densa*, and *Adiantum pedatum* var. *aleuticum* once survived in supraglacial refugia, they and other serpentine endemics seem to have found their way to almost every serpentine outcrop, large or small. Only people seem as persistent in their migrations.

The Caledonian Connection

The Viking adventure didn't really begin as a migration, but rather as hit-and-run attacks by Norwegian and Danish raiders. Appearing in the western seas in the late eighth century, these early Norsemen were despoilers of monasteries, ravagers of villages. Behind their travels was a desire for wealth, and abundant wealth they stole from the monasteries of Britain and the continent—Lindisfarne, Jarrow, Iona, Noirmoutier, Dublin, Hamburg, and Paris. But hidden in this despoliation was the beginning of a migration, one that would eventually bring the Viking God-men to the shores of the New World. Soon after the early raids in northern Britain, the Vikings were settling to farm in Orkney, Shetland, on the north coast of Scotland, and somewhat later, in the Hebrides and Faroes. From the Faroes it was only a short hop to Iceland, and wholesale colonization of this northern island took place between about A.D. 870 and 930. In Iceland the settlers found rich grazing, and with their Norwegian stock and seed they planted their farms in the uninhabited Iceland landscape. But this was only the beginning of their migration.

Around the year A.D. 985 a Norwegian outlaw named Erik the Red settled on the fringe of the inhospitable minicontinent that lay to the west of Iceland—Greenland. At Brattahlid (now known as Qagssiarssuk) Erik and his family built the farm that has in the last half century been laid bare for archaeologists to ponder. Along with the farm buildings there are the remains of a church at Brattahlid, a church built by Erik's Christian wife, Thjodhild. Like plants on an epic migration through time and space to new habitats, the pagan Northmen were changing as they migrated, influenced by their environment as much as they made their mark on it. Christianity was one of the most powerful of the new elements that molded the Vikings, and the men and women who worshiped on long Arctic nights in Thjodhild's turf church were undoubtedly different from the raiders who sacked Lindisfarne two centuries before. One constant remained though, a constant continually reinforced when one strips away soil to see the past, the seminal action of the archaeologist. Christian or pagan, the flesh lives not forever, but is laid bare to bone by time and rust. Today there are skeletons below the green grass that once seemed to drip with butter for those first Greenland settlers. Perhaps they are the bones of Erik the Red and his kin, but Viking chieftain or Pictish slave, there are now only bones in the black turf. Heroic legends may linger in that North Atlantic mist, but there are only bones in the black turf.

So it was, not only for Erik's settlement, but for Greenland's entire population. By A.D. 1500 the Norsemen no longer inhabited Greenland, the extinction due perhaps to the scattered nature of the settlement, the climate, or to the length and difficulty of communication between settlements and with the outside world. One of the theories behind the Greenland "extinction" is that the settlers emigrated to North America, and though this is doubtful, there is no doubt that the Vikings did reach the New World. Both the Groenlandinga (Greenlander's) Saga and Erik's Saga, written in the thirteenth century, detail the fact that in about A.D. 986 Bjarni Herjolfson was driven by a storm to within sight of the coast of North America. The following year, Leif, son of Erik the Red, sailed from Brattahlid in Bjarni's boat to lands he called Helluland (Baffin Island), Markland (Labrador), and Vinland (Newfoundland). The Greenlander's Saga states that Leif built "large houses" there, and Erik's Saga records the journey of three ships to Vinland about a century later.

Though their migration brought them to the New World, the Vikings never put down deep roots here. When John Cabot made his landfall at Cape Bonavista in 1497, he found in the New-founde-Lande no descendants of fearless Vikings. The Norsemen had come and gone centuries before, leaving barely a trace of their brief occupation. England ruled the seas now, and few looked to past Viking glory as a source of pride and inspiration. Newfoundland was to be England's first colony, the breaking crest of a wave of English colonialism that would eventually come ashore on most of the earth's continents and archipelagoes.

Though in Iceland, the Faroes, and Shetland the Viking presence was never forgotten during the centuries of English ascendancy, the Viking heritage was gradually eclipsed elsewhere. Russia exorcised itself of its "Norseness"; once-Viking Normandy became thoroughly French; and in England only linguists and historians held romantic thoughts about Vikings on British soil. That the Viking adventure had before the year A.D. 1000 reached an extraordinary end point of exploration—America—was also forgotten to all but a few scholars of the sagas.

The "rediscovery" of America's discovery came in the late nineteenth century, when great numbers of Scandinavians immigrated to the upper Midwest. Cut from their northern European roots, the need to establish their identity in an alien land led many of the Scandinavian settlers in search of evidence that their ancestors were the first settlers of the New World. These ancestors had come, not as second-class citizens, but as vainglorious warriors who claimed title to most of the known world at that time. If any shadow from history could stir intense pride, surely it was the Viking, and the Viking shadow inspired the immigrants to imagine runic inscriptions on erratic boulders in Minnesota and Scandinavian vocabulary in North American Indian languages. Supposed Viking boats were unearthed from Boston to Bangor, and Leif Eriksson was alleged to have slept in more places than George Washington. Indeed, the pursuit of Viking artifacts—real or imagined—became a small industry in North America. All of the finds, however, from Olaf Ohman's Kensington stone to Yale University's "Vinland Map," were equally spurious.

One of the most recent searchers after the Norse in the New World was a Norwegian explorer and writer named Helge Ingstad. In the 1950s Ingstad conducted extensive examinations of the Norse settlements in southwestern Greenland with his wife, archaeologist Anne Stine Ingstad, and in 1959 they began a search for the "Vinland the Good" of Icelandic sagas. Ingstad at first followed the lead of many scholars, who believed that "vin" referred to the presence of wild grapes in the new land. This interpretation was reinforced by a passage in the Greenlander's Saga, which tells the story of one of Leif's crew, Tyrkir the German, going into the woods near their camp and finding wild grapes. Since the northern limit of wild grapes along the Atlantic Coast was in southern New Brunswick, Ingstad concentrated his search south of there, scouring the New England coast for a sign of Viking occupation. Though this search was unsuccessful, Ingstad persevered. Aware of another interpretation of the sagas, that the Old Norse word *vin* referred not to grapes, but to a meadow or pasture, he shifted his search farther north to the island of Newfoundland. Others had previously identified Newfoundland as the probable site of the first Viking landfall; in 1929 W. A. Munn, a Newfoundland historian, had presented a convincing case that the area around Pistolet Bay at the northern tip of Newfoundland was the likely site of Vinland the Good. Munn visualized the Vikings sailing south along the Labrador coast, crossing the Straits of Belle Isle, and landing at a place called L'Anse aux Meadows. From there he believed that the Viking explorers would have sailed around Cape Onion into Pistolet Bay and perhaps have settled on the shores of Milan Arm. Munn's theories had spurred Danish archaeologist Jørgen Meldgaard to conduct excavations around Pistolet Bay in the mid-1950s. Though Meldgaard's research had yielded nothing, Ingstad zeroed in on the same region at the end of his 1959 survey. Returning the next summer, Ingstad was making queries in the tiny village of L'Anse aux Meadows when a fisherman named Joe Dekker told him about some interesting humps and depressions that marked a place near the village—the locals called it "Indian Camp." Though meant as a joke, Ingstad took the suggestion seriously, and when he first viewed the faint outlines in the contours of the land at Indian Camp, they looked eerily familiar. The image of Brattahlid and its sister settlements in Greenland came to mind, and Ingstad decided that the site was worth excavating.

In 1961, under the direction of Anne Stine Ingstad, excavation began on the grassy mounds that dotted the curving marine terrace that lies about 100 meters from the present shore of Épaves Bay (*see Map 8*). (A thousand years ago, the shore lay only a few meters away, the land here not having fully rebounded from the removal of its glacial burden.) It was quickly ascertained that the mounds were the lower courses of the walls of turf buildings. There seemed to be three large dwellings, four workshops or boat sheds, and even a smithy. The layout of one of the buildings resembled a "great hall" of true Viking style, and fire pits in the centers of the dwellings suggested those unearthed at known Viking settlements, including Brattahlid. The smithy contained scant but incontrovertible evidence of iron-working in the form of forging slag and a furnace pit for smelting iron by means of charcoal.

Despite all this evidence that the Ingstads had uncovered the first known Viking settlement in North America, skepticism greeted their finds. The academic world had been duped more than once regarding "Viking finds," and scholars were guarded in their enthusiasm

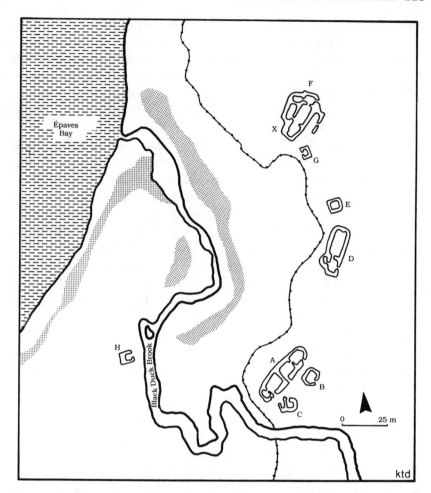

MAP 8   Map of L'Anse aux Meadows archaeological site showing Norse house sites (A–G), smithy (H), and the location of the Norse spindle-whorl discovery (x). Shaded areas are Atlantic-type meadows that give the area its contemporary name and may have inspired the Viking name "Vinland." The shoreline that dates to the time of Norse occupation at L'Anse aux Meadows is also indicated (➔➔➔). (After Wallace, 1977, and Kuc, 1975)

over the discovery. After three summers of intensive fieldwork, not a single Norse artifact had been uncovered, and this seemed suspect if the sod houses at L'Anse aux Meadows had indeed been built by Vikings. This fact had not gone unnoticed by Helge Ingstad, who despite his faith in the authenticity of his discovery, secretly hoped for the recovery of an artifact of indisputably Norse origin. Ingstad had sometimes dreamed of a large, fine Viking sword appearing in the earth, or of a hunting knife, but he knew that such objects would have been coveted by the natives of the area, and hence would have been carried off by them. He knew equally that such prized possessions as these would have been carefully stewarded by any Viking so far from his native land. That a sword or hunting knife should have ever remained behind was extremely unlikely.

By the summer of 1964 the excavation team had grown to include other professionals and amateurs interested in the L'Anse aux Meadows site. The 1964 expedition included Dr. Junius Bird of the American Museum of Natural History and his wife, Peggy; Birgitta Wallace of the Carnegie Museum in Pittsburgh; and Tony Beardsley, a young Canadian. It was Beardsley who, on August 4, 1964, made the discovery that Helge Ingstad had been so fervently hoping for and that ranks as one of the great finds in North American archaeology. Beardsley was excavating a test trench along the wall of the southernmost room of the largest house site. As he dug through the turf he found a tiny stone ring. He gave out a yell, and the other archaeologists rushed to look at his find. Anne Stine Ingstad, Birgitta Wallace, and Junius Bird hugged each other as they realized that their discovery had at last been confirmed. The stone ring was a steatite spindle whorl, used during Viking times to spin wool, and it was practically identical in style to spindle whorls dug up from Norse settlements in Greenland, Iceland, and Norway.

The inch-wide soapstone object was far more significant than a Viking sword, for it told the archaeologists that among the people who lived at L'Anse aux Meadows almost a thousand years ago there had probably been women, and that they must have had wool from which to spin thread. In this new, unknown land, Viking women once sat spinning in that sunny southern room, facing the sun and sea and sheltered from the cold north winds, fashioning thread in their tenuous attempt to settle the New-Founde-Lande.

Having found a Norse site, did the sagas confirm L'Anse aux Meadows as the place of Leif Eriksson's landfall in Vinland?

They sailed in towards it [the land] and came to an island which lay north of the land. There they went ashore and looked around, and the weather was fine. They saw that there was dew on the grass, and it came that they got some of it on their hands and put it to their lips, and they thought that they had never tasted anything so sweet.

They then returned to their ship and sailed into the sound which lay between the island and the cape projecting north-ward from the mainland. They sailed westward past the cape. It was very shallow there at low tide. Their ship went aground, and it was a long way from the ship to the sea. But they were so impatient to get to land that they did not want to wait for the tide to rise under their ship but ran ashore at a place where a river flowed out of a lake.

So goes the saga of Erik the Red, written down on parchment in Iceland some two hundred years after the event. The Greenlander's Saga, though believed to have been produced independently at around the same time, tells a closely parallel story. Both of the sagas accurately describe the landscape in the vicinity of the L'Anse aux Meadows site. There is a pronounced cape pointing north, with an island, Great Sacred Island, to the north of it. The bay directly below the Norse sites is so shallow that the sea floor lies exposed for a great distance at low tide. The "large houses" that the saga says Leif built in Vinland are there, and so too are the meadows that would have looked inviting to the Norse herdsmen. As for wild grapes, perhaps the Vikings referred to the large cloudberries (*Rubus chamaemorus*) that grow in the bogs nearby the site.

Saga is an old Norse word that comes from the root "to say," and though voiceless, the little steatite spindle whorl contains a saga as compelling as that recorded on the Iceland parchments. Though there are soapstone deposits in Greenland and in Norway, deposits worked by the Vikings, the spindle whorl at L'Anse aux Meadows did not come from these homeland places. It came instead from the New World, but not directly from some outcrop discovered by the Vikings, for the spindle whorl found at L'Anse aux Meadows is a fragment of an old soapstone oil lamp. The bottom of the spindle whorl is con-cave and blackened by soot, and this soot must have been there before the spindle whorl was made, since the edges, which were rounded during the process of manufacture, showed no traces of soot.

Confirmation of the possibility that the Norse may have encoun-tered native steatite artifacts came later during the excavations, when a soapstone lamp was discovered on the floor of the smithy along Black Duck Brook. It was exactly the sort of lamp that may have provided the raw material for the spindle whorl. The style of the lamp showed it to be the product of the Dorset culture, which had advanced across the North American Arctic into Newfoundland by about 100 B.C. Lamps such as the one found in the smithy had made this expansion possible, since the tundra provided little fuel for heating and cooking. To hold off the cold, dark Arctic night, the Dorset people had fashioned stone lamps that held a different fuel—fish and seal oil. It was this same long Arctic night that gave rise to the singular artistry of the Dorset people, who filled their nocturnal hours by carving on pendants and amulets of whalebone. Two thousand years later their Inuit descendants would turn their artistry to a new material—soapstone—to the delight of a mystery-starved Anglo art world.

The Dorset culture had faded some two hundred years before the arrival of the Norse, but just as we find trash from the Vikings, the Vikings likely found the refuse of those before them. Both the intact Dorset soapstone lamp from the smithy and the one that became a Norse spindle whorl probably were found at an old Dorset encampment in the area along the shores of Épaves Bay. (Numerous native sites predating the Norse settlement have been identified there.) The source of steatite for the Dorset themselves would seem most likely to have been the Fleur de Lys soapstone quarry, which lies some 175 kilometers to the south, at the tip of the Baie Verte Peninsula. There, at the end of a footpath running behind one of the houses of the little fishing village of Fleur de Lys, stands a stretch of cliff perhaps 15 meters high, 200 meters long. The entire face of the cliff is marked by excavated hollows in orderly lines, the scars made by ancient quarry workers when they removed the bowl "preforms." Stand there and you are standing at the Ochee Springs quarry, the Broad Creek quarry, Holmes's Connecticut Avenue quarries. Stand there on a day in August and it is the same—the Newfoundland air is a bit cooler; surrounding you are spruce and fir, not oak and hickory; and the nearby bedrock from which you might fashion your quarrying tools is different, but the similarity is unmistakable. The harebells that grow all over the edges of the quarry take one back to the cliffs at the big bend of the Octoraro Creek, or to the dunite escarpments in the Green Mountains. The cliff-face quarry speaks of continuity— the sinuous thread that is time and its occupants is as continuous as the Appalachians. The gaps, the breaks, the hiatuses are brief and easily overcome by imagination.

The spectacular workings on the cliff at Fleur de Lys need little imagining. The hundreds of circular recesses show that the Dorset people quarried soapstone there, but was it indeed a Fleur de Lys soapstone lamp that eventually became the Norse spindle whorl found at L'Anse aux Meadows? This question of the source of an artifact, a fundamental clue to patterns of prehistoric resource use, has plagued archaeologists from F. W. Putnam and W. H. Holmes to William Fowler. It is of even more interest to contemporary archaeologists, who have begun to consider archaic human ecology in terms of energetics and systems dynamics. Processing with computers the records of over a century of archaeological data, they can generate "random walk" resource procurement patterns of people long vanished.

The procurement patterns of soapstone, which has discrete and localized sources, has always been somewhat easier to imagine than broadly distributed rocks such as quartz or chert. Still, it has always been impossible to prove from which particular prehistoric quarry any given steatite artifact has come. Quarries closest to the site of the artifact were usually presumed to be the source. In the last decade, however, archaeologists have made use of a chemical technique that precisely matches steatite artifacts to their source. The technique, called neutron activation analysis, uses the unique trace element chemistry of soapstone to "fingerpaint" artifacts and quarry samples. Because the trace element contents are determined by the metamorphic process at a particular locality, and because this process differs between areas, the trace element chemistry of soapstone within any one outcrop is usually distinct from that of other regions. Using this technique, archaeologists have pinpointed the origin of late Woodland period smoking pipes found in places hundreds of miles from steatite sources—Ohio, Kentucky, Indiana, and elsewhere. The results have shown that most of the eastern quarries—from Ochee Springs in Rhode Island to the Albemarle region quarries in Virginia—supplied steatite objects for trade in the sixth to fifteenth centuries A.D. At a more local level, archaeologists have modeled steatite trade patterns between the Piedmont and Coastal Plain regions of Virginia.

A few years ago William Fitzhugh of the Smithsonian Institution moved the technique north to cipher out the movement of soapstone along the Labrador coast. Collaborating with chemists from the University of Virginia, Fitzhugh analyzed over sixty steatite artifacts recovered at Labrador sites of both the Dorset culture (lamps and bowls) and that of the Maritime Archaic "Indians" (plummets or "net sinkers"). Using neutron activation analysis, they found that at least eight soapstone sources have been used over the last four thousand years. Of these eight, only four have been located. Two of the source quarries were in Labrador, one at Freestone (a traditional name for soapstone) Habour in the Davis Inlet area south of Nain, and the other at Moores Island near Okak, north of Nain. These two deposits lie outside the Appalachian realm, and though emplaced in the North American craton through the same process of obduction as the Appalachian soapstone deposits, the Labrador steatite is vastly older, dating from orogenic events in the Precambrian.

The other two quarry sources identified are indeed "Appalachian," one being the large outcrop at Fleur de Lys. The final quarry lies less than a mile from the embankments of tumbled turf walls at L'Anse aux Meadows. Plotted on a graph of trace element concentrations, the pattern for the L'Anse aux Meadows quarry and the Norse spindle whorl are almost an exact fit. It is sheer serendipity that any source of the soft stone ended up so close to the L'Anse aux Meadows site. The country rock is all sedimentary—the flats upon which the Norse site lies are underlain by black shale, while a few hundred yards to the southwest, where it is marked by a pronounced escarpment, the land is all greywacke, conglomerate, and sandstone.

The zone of black shale that harbors the source block of soapstone is not homogeneous, but is rather a mélange of fragmented and mixed rock types. Exotic blocks of serpentine, pillow lava, and other rocks are mixed at random through the shale matrix. As much as the complete ophiolites that dot the Appalachian orogen, the mélange speaks of ancient plate movements, the exotic blocks representing megadebris from the obduction process that settled to the ocean floor.

The particular piece of debris that furnished the Dorset lamp—become—Norse spindle whorl is an exotic block of serpentine about 350 feet long and 100 feet wide. Within the block are northeast-trending zones of steatite that developed during the transport process way back in the Middle Ordovician. They are small zones, only a few feet wide, hardly providing the possibility for quarrying that the cliff at Fleur de Lys does. But small as these zones are, they are soap-stone, and they must have begged to be quarried, shaped, carved as surely as the exotic blocks flanking Bell's Mill Road on the Wissa-hickon beg to be carved. If the Viking adventure had really taken root, if the Norse had stayed longer at the meadows on Épaves Bay, perhaps they would have found the little serpentine hill that held the source of their spindle whorl. If they'd stayed, perhaps there would be Norse-style hollows in the thin steatite layer, and fragments of iron adzes wrought from their New World smithy on Black Duck Brook would mingle with the soapstone talus at the base of the hill.

But they didn't stay. They returned to their homeland on the other side of the North Atlantic. When they touched shore in Ireland, in Scotland, the Shetlands, or the fjords of Norway, the returning Vikings were touching shore that was once linked with the rocks of their New World landfall. The plate tectonic vision that unraveled the mysteries of Appalachian geology has also revealed that the northern extremity of the Appalachians in Newfoundland and the western ex-tremity of the Caledonides in Ireland were once almost continguous. Beyond Ireland, the British Caledonides stretch through Scotland, England, Wales, and Shetland, with natural continuations north-ward through East Greenland and Scandinavia and beyond to Spitz-bergen on the Arctic Circle. All the main structural elements of the British Caledonides, from the Hebridean foreland south across the deformed zone of Dalradian (the Caledonian equivalent of "Gren-villian"—that is, Precambrian) rocks and the Midland Valley to the Precambrian and Cambrian rocks of the Welsh Borderlands, can be matched with similar elements in the northern Appalachians. In fact, the geology of Newfoundland, the northern extremity of the Ap-palachian orogen, is more akin to that of the British Isles than it is to parts of the southern Appalachians.

The way geologists have approached the comparison of the Ap-palachian-Caledonian rocks is by recognizing a small number of contrasting tectonic-stratigraphic zones across the entire system. The zonal system of Harold Williams (1978) of the Memorial Univer-sity of Newfoundland has proven most useful in such comparisons. Recognizing four major divisions, each extrapolated over the full length of the system from Newfoundland to Alabama, Williams has named (from west to east) the following broad zones: Humber, Dun-nage, Gander, and Avalon. Each of these names derives from local place-names in Newfoundland. In the Caledonides, a similar four-fold subdivision has been outlined by Williams (1978), each British zone being assigned a local name with phonetics similar to that of the name of the comparable zone in Newfoundland: Hebrides (Humber), Dundee (Dunnage), Greenore (Gander), Anglesey (Avalon; *see Map 9*).

In tracing the serpentine tale, we have been wandering mainly in the Humber zone. It is this zone that harbors the Blue-Green-Long line, the imaginary demarcation created by the three large inliers of Precambrian crystalline basement—the Blue Ridge, Green Mountains, and Long Range of Newfoundland. The Cambrian-Ordovician carbonate sequence overlying the basement can be traced from western Newfoundland to the Valley and Ridge Province of the southern Appalachians. The mélange that makes up the L'Anse aux Meadows country rock has analogs through much of Quebec and the Gaspé, with southern equivalents in the Taconic Range of New York and the Hamburg klippen of Pennsylvania. Ophiolite suites like the one containing the Fleur de Lys quarry can be traced to Mont Albert and on south through the Eastern Townships of Quebec, through Vermont and Massachusetts to Staten Island and the lower Susquehanna River deposits.

If we were to continue tracing the Appalachian ultramafics across the Atlantic to their Caledonian counterparts, we would concentrate our traverse in the Hebrides zone. There the Grenvillian basement rocks of the Long Range are represented in West Ireland by billion-year-old gneisses and granites, in Scotland by the Lewisian complex basement to the Outer Hebrides, which give the zone its name. The Highland Boundary Fault, which delineates the Hebrides zone to the south, appears to be a natural continuation of Newfoundland's Baie Verte Lineament.

As for serpentine endemics and outcrops of "asaxusas," they too have their analogs. The Hebridean zone in Norway has the Jootedals, northern mountains that furnished the big soapstone blocks for Viking campfires and spindle whorls for their weaving wives. The Caledonides have their own equivalent of Mont Albert and Table Mountain also—the Keen of Hamar on the island of Unst in the Shetlands. Though lower in elevation, the plants harbored by the ultramafic rock there are often familiar. Wide-ranging taxa like ferns and grasses are there in *Asplenium viride* (which occurs on ultramafics in Quebec and on one outcrop in Maine), *Deschampsia caespitosa*, and *Festuca rubra* (the fescue grass of Quebec and Newfoundland's

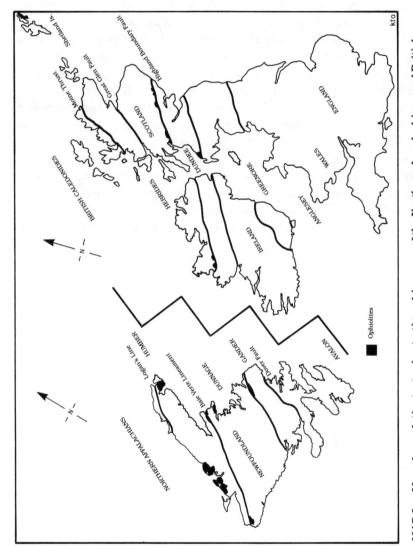

MAP 9 Map of correlative tectonic-stratigraphic zones of the Northern Appalachians and British Caledonides. (After Williams, 1978b)

serpentine barrens). Other species identical to those of the Appalachian ultramafics—*Campanula rotundifolia, Silene acaulis, Juniperis communis, Achillea millefolium*—are there also, and the Caryophyllaceae, that family ubiquitous to ultramafics everywhere, has its representatives in a number of *Cerastium*s and *Arenaria*s.

The other zones—Dunnage/Dundee, Gander/Greenore, Avalon/Anglesey—each have their own set of parallel lithologies and tectonics, and their own tales of past cultures, prehistoric quarrying, and historic events. From the Anglesey zone of the Caledonides to the Avalon zone at Plymouth Rock came the settlers of the New World (sparked by the outcome of a conference between King James and the Puritans at Hampton Court Palace in London in 1604). The Avalonian terrain was cast in the same mold as its Anglesey counterpart across the Atlantic, and its rocks got here before the Pilgrims. Pilgrims, Vikings, Paleo-Indians, canoe-wanderers on the Susquehanna, Victorian geologists, and bicycle-riding botanists—we have all followed the earth events played out on the Appalachian orogen.

Conclusion

The serpentine spots marking the ancient geosuture that threads along the length of the Appalachians are special places—they mark locations of unique habitats, unique cultural activities, and unique geological histories. This uniqueness seems fitting, since they are the only sites in the entire mountain chain that have an origin wholly different from the rest of the rocks. Quartzites, sandstones, limestones, and the other sedimentary and metamorphic rocks all derive from the detritus of continental materials. Even the igneous intrusions that dot the Appalachians are crustal in origin. Serpentine, dunite, steatite, and related ultramafic rocks are the sole representatives of the earth's mantle, a region hidden from our view.

"Special places" have always interested us. Whether sacred or secular, we have spent millennia divining them, by searching for the reasons behind their uniqueness, using the basic technique of natural history—close observation—to do so. In the process we have "divined" these places in a different sense, the sense of empowering them, making them sacred or divine by our very efforts. Each prehistoric steatite quarry, each serpentine barren along the Appalachian orogen is a shrine of sorts, testimony to both the permanence of time and the impermanence of us and our "divining."

This "natural history" is quite incomplete, since there are hosts of other special serpentine places in the Appalachians. But no natural history is ever complete, offering instead an entry point for new observations and interpretations. Whether approached with scientific questions in mind, or with the desire to be in touch with past peoples and events, each serpentine spot presents each explorer with his or her own possibility.

Glossary

aborigines original inhabitants of an area

acidophilous restricted to acid-rich soils

adit a nearly horizontal passage into a mine

allochthonous rocks that have not been formed in situ

anticlinal inclined toward each other

Archaic the prehistoric period designated by archaeologists between 8000 to 1000 B.C.

Archean ancient; the term generally has been applied to the oldest rocks of the Precambrian

arkose a sandstone containing 25 percent or more of feldspars usually derived from silicic igneous rocks

asbestos fibrous form of serpentine

atlatl a device for throwing a spear

autochthonous rocks that have been formed in situ

basement the complex of igneous and metamorphic rocks that are overlain unconformably by sedimentary strata

basiphilous restricted to base-rich soils

calciphilous more or less restricted to limestone soils

calciphyte a plant with an affinity for limy soils

Cenozoic the latest of the four eras into which geologic time is divided

chert a dense, glassy stone usually found in limestone outcrops; it was the most popular material for chipped stone tools in eastern North America; sometimes called flint, jasper, or chalcedony

chromite a mineral—$(MgFe^{+2})(CrAlFe^{+2})_2O_4$—that is the principal ore of chromium

chrysotile highly fibrous variety of serpentine

cinnabar the mineral HgS; the principal ore of mercury

clastic consisting of fragments of rock or organic structures that have been moved from their place of origin

Coastal Plain the Atlantic Coastal Plain of North America

congener a member of the same genus

conglomerate rounded water-worn fragments of rock or pebbles cemented together by another mineral substance

continental drift the concept that the continents can drift on the surface of the earth because of the weakness of the suboceanic crust

country rock a general term applied to the rock surrounding and penetrated by mineral veins or an igneous intrusion

craton large, immobile part of the earth's crust

diabase basaltic rock

dike a tabular body of igneous rock that cuts across the structure of adjacent rocks

dip the angle at which a bed or planar feature is inclined from the horizontal; perpendicular to the strike direction

disjunction anomalous plant distribution involving a large distance from the nearest other occurrence

dolomite calcium magnesium carbonate

dunite an ultramafic rock composed almost entirely of olivine

edaphic environmental conditions due to soil or topography rather than climate

endemic native or restricted to a particular region

ericaceous a member of the Ericaceae, the heath family

escarpment a steep face terminating highlands abruptly

eugeosyncline (eugeocline) a geosyncline in which vulcanism is associated with sedimentation

fault a fracture or fracture zone along which there has been displacement of the sides relative to each other parallel to the fracture

floristics the branch of phytogeography that deals numerically with plants and plant groups

fluted point any of several Paleo-Indian period point types having long, thinning flakes struck from their sides

foreland the region in front of a series of overthrust sheets

glabrate smooth

gneiss coarse-grained granitic rock

graben a block downthrown along faults relative to the rocks on either side

greywacke a coarse, usually dark gray sandstone or fine-grained conglomerate composed of firmly cemented rounded fragments (as of quartz or feldspars)

herbarium an institute where dried plants are stored for scientific study

Hypsithermal postglacial warm interval from about 7000 to 600 B.C.; also called the "climactic optimum" or "thermal maximum"

ice age a glacial period or part of a glacial period, usually the last (Pleistocene) glacial period

klippen an isolated block of rocks separated from the underlying rocks by a fault that normally has a gentle dip

lanceolate lance-shaped

magma naturally occurring mobile rock material, generated within the earth and capable of intrusion and extrusion

magnesite magnesium mineral composed mainly of magnesium carbonate

mantle the layer of the earth between the crust and the core

mid-oceanic ridge the continuous, seismic, median mountain range extending through the oceans and believed to be the source of new crustal material

miogeosyncline (miogeocline) a geosyncline in which vulcanism is not associated with sedimentation

mesophytic growing under medium conditions of soil moisture

morphology the study of form

Neolithic in Europe, the latest period of the Stone Age, characterized by polished stone implements

obduction the sliding of one plate over another

ophiolite an assemblage of mafic and ultramafic igneous rocks whose origin is associated with an early phase in the development of a geosyncline

orogen belt of deformed rocks (for example, the Appalachian orogen)

orogeny the process of forming mountains

Paleo-Indian people inhabiting North America from 10,500 to 8000 B.C.

Paleolithic in Europe, the latest period of the Stone Age characterized by rough, chipped stone implements

Paleozoic the era of geologic time between the Precambrian and the Mesozoic, comprising the Cambrian, Ordovician, Silurian, Devonian, Carboniferous, and Permian systems

peneplain a land surface worn down by erosion to a nearly flat or broadly undulating plain

peridotite coarse-grained ultramafic rock consisting principally of olivine and pyroxene

phenology the study of the relations between climate and periodic phenomena (for example, flowering, fruiting)

phyllite an argillaceous (composed of clay minerals) rock intermediate in metamorphic grade between slate and schist

phytosociology the study of plant communities

Piedmont the Appalachian geomorphic province lying between the Ridge and Valley and Coastal Plain provinces

plant community an interacting population of various plant species in a common location

plate large segment of the earth's crust varying in thickness from 30 to 150 miles

Pleistocene the earlier of the two epochs that make up the Quaternary period

pluton body of igneous rock formed beneath the surface of the earth by consolidation from magma

quartzite compact granular rock composed of quartz and derived from sandstone by metamorphism

Quaternary the younger of the two geologic periods making up the Cenozoic Era; subdivided into the Pleistocene and Holocene epochs

red beds term applied to red sedimentary rocks, usually sandstone and shale

rhyolite a very acid volcanic rock that is the extrusive (lava) form of granite

schist medium- or coarse-grained granitic rock

serpentine a mineral group with the general formula $(MgFe)_3Si_2O_5(OH)_4$; the group includes the minerals antigorite and chrysotile and is characterized by long, fibrous crystals

serpentinite a rock formed principally from serpentine minerals

silicate a salt of any of the silicic acids

soapstone a massive, impure variety of talc

steatite massive, usually impure, talc-rich rock

steatization formation of talc-rich rocks

strike the bearing of the outcrop of an inclined bed on a level surface; perpendicular to the direction of the dip

talc a mineral whose formula is $Mg_3Si_4O_{10}(OH)_2$

talus disintegrated rocky material forming a slope at the foot of a steeper declivity

tectonic pertaining to the rock structure and external forms resulting from the deformation of the earth's crust

Terminal Archaic the prehistoric time period between 1700 to 700 B.C.

Tertiary the older of the two geologic periods that make up the Ceno-zoic Era; the strata deposited during that period

Transitional period the prehistoric time period between 1300 to 1000 B.C.

trap rock the term applied to dark-colored dike and flow rocks, chiefly basalt and diabase

Triassic the earliest of the three periods of the Mesozoic

ultramafic igneous rock with less than 45 percent silica and com-posed principally of ferromagnesian minerals

uniformitarianism the belief that the present is the key to the past

verde-antique a dark green rock usually crisscrossed with white veinlets of magnesium or calcium carbonates, composed essen-tially of serpentine and often used as an ornamental stone

villose hairy

xeric dry

xerophytic growing under dry conditions

Bibliography

Introduction

Brewer, W. H. 1930. Up and Down California in 1860–1864: The Journal of William H. Brewer. New Haven: Yale University Press.

Brooks, R. R. 1987. *Serpentine and Its Vegetation: A Multidisciplinary Approach.* Portland, Oreg.: Dioscorides Press.

Coleman, R. G. 1977. *Ophiolites: Ancient Oceanic Lithosphere?* New York: Springer.

Ericson, P. J., and B. Purdy, eds. 1984. *Prehistoric Quarries and Lithic Production.* Cambridge: Cambridge University Press.

Wyllie, P. J., ed. 1978. *Ultramafic and Related Rocks.* New York: Wiley.

Asaxusas

Brown, A. K. 1967. *The Aboriginal Population of the Santa Barbara Channel.* University of California Archaeology Survey Reports 69. Berkeley: University of California Press.

Hinsley, C. M. 1981. *Savages and Scientists: The Smithsonian Institution and the Development of American Anthropology, 1846–1910.* Washington, D.C.: Smithsonian Institution Press.

Holmes, W. H. 1897. Stone implements of the Potomac-Chesapeake Tidewater Province. *Fifteenth Annual Report of the Bureau of American Ethnology,* 13–152.

Humphrey, R. L., and M. E. Chambers. 1977. *Ancient Washington: American Indian Cultures of the Potomac Valley.* George Washington Studies no. 6. Washington, D.C.: George Washington University.

Manson, Carl. 1948. Marcey Creek site: an early manifestation in the Potomac Valley. *American Antiquity* 13(3):223–227.

Snow, D. R. 1976. *Archaeology of North America.* New York: Viking.

Turnbaugh, W. A. 1975. Toward an explanation of the broadpoint dispersal in eastern North American prehistory. *Journal of Anthropological Research* 31(1):51–68.

Witthoft, J. 1953. Broad spearpoints and the transitional period cultures. *Pennsylvania Archaeologist* 23(1):4–31.

Holmes's Hope

Heizer, R. F. 1941. The distribution and name of the Chumash plank canoe. *Masterkey* 15:59–61.

Holmes, W. H. 1928. Random Records of a Lifetime. Unpublished manuscript. W. H. Holmes Papers, National Anthropological Archives, Smithsonian Institution, Washington, D.C.

Kroeber, A. 1925. Handbook of the Indians of California. *U.S. Bureau of American Ethnology Bulletin* 78:550–568.

Mohr, A., and L. L. Sample. 1955. The religious importance of the swordfish in the Santa Barbara Channel. *Masterkey* 29:62–68.

Rogers, D. B. 1929. *Prehistoric Man of the Santa Barbara Coast.* Santa Barbara, Calif.: Santa Barbara Museum of Natural History.

Yates, L. G. 1889. Charm stones: notes on the so-called "plummets" or sinkers. *Smithsonian Institution Annual Report for 1886* (1):296–305.

Strange Plantscape on the Octoraro

Braun-Blanquet, J. 1932. *Plant Sociology: The Study of Plant Communities.* Translated by G. D. Fuller and H. S. Conance. New York: McGraw-Hill.

Clements, F. E. 1916. *Plant Succession: An Analysis of the Development of Vegetation.* Washington, D.C.: Carnegie Institute.

Earnest, E. P. 1940. *John and William Bartram: Botanists and Explorers.* Philadelphia: University of Pennsylvania Press.

Gleason, H. A. 1926. The individualistic concept of the plant association. *Bulletin of the Torrey Botanical Club* 53:7–26.

Pennell, F. W. 1930. On some critical species of the serpentine barrens. *Bartonia* 12:1–23.

Proctor, J., and S. R. J. Woodell. 1975. The ecology of serpentine soils. *Advances in Ecological Research* (9):255–366.

Tansley, A. G. 1920. The classification of vegetation and the concepts of development. *Journal of Ecology* 8:118–149.

Whittaker, R. H. 1954. The ecology of serpentine soils. *Ecology* 35:258–259.

———. 1962. Classification of natural communities. *Botanical Review* 28:1–239.

Taxonomic Tangles

American Philosophical Society. 1744. Charter of the American Philosophical Society. *American Philosophical Society Transactions* 1.

Darlington, W. 1837. *Flore Cestrica*. Philadelphia: Lindsay and Blakiston.

Mears, J. A. 1980. The relevance of plant collections at the Academy of Natural Sciences of Philadelphia to Torrey and Gray's *Flora of the North America, 1838–1842*. *Proceedings of the Academy of National Sciences of Philadelphia* 132:228–238.

———. 1981. Guide to plant collectors represented in the herbarium of the Academy of Natural Sciences of Philadelphia. *Proceedings of the Academy of Natural Sciences of Philadelphia* 133:141–165.

Muhlenberg, H. 1813. *Catalogus Plantarum Americae Septentrionalis: A Catalog of the Hitherto Known Native and Naturalized Plants of North America Arranged According to the Sexual System of Linnaeus*. Philadelphia: Solomon W. Conrad.

Pennell, F. W. 1910. Flora of the Conowingo barrens of southeastern Pennsylvania. *Proceedings of the Academy of Natural Sciences of Philadelphia* 62:541–584.

———. 1912. Further notes on the flora of the Conowingo or serpentine barrens of southeastern Pennsylvania. *Proceedings of the Academy of Natural Sciences of Philadelphia* 64:520–539.

———. 1930. On some critical species of the serpentine barrens. *Bartonia* 12:1–23.

Pursh, F. 1824. *Flore Americae Septentrionalis; or a Systematic Arrangement and Description of the Plants of North America.* London: White, Cochrane.

Rafinesque, C. 1808. *Med. Repos. New York* 2(5):359.

Torrey, J. 1824. *A Flora of the Northern and Middle Sections of the United States.* New York: Putnam.

Wherry, E. T. 1963. Some Pennsylvania barrens and their flora. I— Serpentine. *Bartonia* 33:7–11.

The Serpentine Gestalt

Hart, R. 1980. Coexistence of weeds and restricted native plants of serpentine barrens in southeastern Pennsylvania. *Ecology* 61(3):688–701.

Lines and Holes

Hall, C. E. 1881. *The Geology of Philadelphia County and of the Southern Parts of Montgomery and Bucks.* Second Geological Survey of Pennsylvania Report of Progress C6.

———. 1885. *Field Notes on Delaware County.* Second Geological Survey of Pennsylvania Report of Progress C5. Part 1.

Lesley, J. P., ed. 1883. *The Geology of Chester County, after the Surveys of Henry D. Rogers, Persifor Frazer, and Charles E. Hall.* Second Geological Survey of Pennsylvania Report of Progress C4.

Mathews, E. B. 1908. History of the boundary dispute between the Baltimores and Penns resulting in the original Mason and Dixon line. *Maryland Geological Survey* 7:103–202.

Window on the Appalachians

Frazer, P. 1880. *The Geology of Lancaster County.* Second Geological Survey of Pennsylvania Report of Progress C3.

Lesley, J. P. 1876. *Historical sketch of geological exploration in Pennsylvania and other states.* Published by the Board of Commissioners for the Second Geological Survey of Pennsylvania.

Lesley, J. P., ed. 1883. *The Geology of Chester County, after the Surveys of Henry D. Rogers, Persifor Frazer, and Charles E. Hall.* Second Geological Survey of Pennsylvania Report of Progress C4.

Rogers, H. D., and W. B. Rogers. 1843. On the physical structure of the Appalachian Chain, as exemplifying the laws which have regulated the elevation of great mountain chains generally. *Transactions of the American Association of Geologists and Naturalists* 1:475–531.

Schneer, C. J. 1979. *Two Hundred Years of Geology in America.* Hanover, N.H.: University Press of New England.

Time and Rust

Brongniart, A. 1829. *Tableau des terrains qui composent l'écorce du globe; ou Essai sur la structure de la partie connue de la terre.* Paris: F. G. Levrault.

Cole, T. No date. *Sketchbook No. 1.* Detroit: Detroit Institute of Arts.

Dana, J. D. 1875. *Manual of Geology.* New York: Ivison, Blakeman, Taylor.

Hayden, H. H. 1833. Description of the Bare Hills near Baltimore. *American Journal of Science* 24:349–363.

Lyell, C. 1830. *Principles of Geology.* New York: D. Appleton.

Ochee Springs

Fowler, W. 1945. Tool-making at the Westfield steatite quarry. *American Antiquity* 11(1):95–101.

———. 1966. The Horne Hill soapstone quarry. *Massachusetts Archaeological Society Bulletin* 27(2):17–28.

———. 1971. Ragged Mountain shelter quarry. *Massachusetts Archaeological Society Bulletin* 32(3–4):9.

————. 1975. The diagnostic stone bowl industry. *Massachusetts Archaeological Society Bulletin* 36(3–4):1–10.

Holmes, W. H. 1897. Stone implements of the Potomac-Chesapeake Tidewater Province. *Fifteenth Annual Report of the Bureau of American Ethnology*, 13–152.

Putnam, F. W. 1878. The manufacture of soapstone pots by the Indians of New England. *Report of the Peabody Museum* 2(18): 273–276.

Turnbaugh, W. A., and T. Kiefer. 1979. Chemical variation in selected soapstone quarries of southern New England. *Man in the Northeast* 18:32–47.

Mystery Pendants on the Missisquoi

Cady, W. M., A. L. Albee, and A. H. Chidester. 1963. Bedrock geology and asbestos deposits of the Upper Missisquoi Valley and vicinity, Vermont. *United States Geological Survey Bulletin* 1122-B.

Chidester, A. H., A. L. Albee, and W. M. Cady. 1978. Petrology, structure, and genesis of the asbestos-bearing ultramafic rocks of the Belvidere Mountain area in Vermont. *United States Geological Survey Professional Paper* 1016.

Johnson, C. W. 1980. *The Nature of Vermont.* Hanover, N.H.: University Press of New England.

Mason, R. J. 1962. The Paleo-Indian in the eastern U.S. *Current Anthropology* 3(3):29–36.

Ritchie, W. A. 1953. A probable Paleo-Indian site in Vermont. *American Antiquity* 18(3):249–258.

The Emergence of Plate Tectonics

Coleman, R. G. 1977. *Ophiolites: Ancient Oceanic Lithosphere?* Berling: Springer-Verlag.

Dana, J. D. 1863. *Manual of Geology.* New York: Ivison, Blakeman, Taylor.

————. 1873. On some results of earth contraction from cooling. *American Journal of Science* 105:423–443.

Dietz, R. S. 1961. Continent and ocean basin evolution by spreading of the sea-floor. *Nature* 190:854–857.

———. 1972. Geosynclines, mountains, and continent-building. *Scientific American* 226(3):30–38.

Fisher, O. 1881. *Physics of the Earth's Crust.* New York: Macmillan.

Hall, J. 1859. Description and figures of the organic remains of the lower Helderburg group and the Oriskany sandstone. *New York Geological Survey, Natural History of New York, Part 6, Paleontology* 3(1).

Hess, H. H. 1962. History of ocean basins. In *Petrologic Studies: A Volume to Honor A. F. Buddington,* edited by A. E. J. Engel, H. L. James, and B. F. Leonard, pp. 599–620. New York: Geological Society of America.

Holmes, W. H. 1928. Random Records of a Lifetime. Unpublished manuscript. W. H. Holmes Papers, National Anthropological Archives, Smithsonian Institution, Washington, D.C.

McKenzie, D. P. 1969. Speculations on the causes and consequences of plate motions. *Geophysical Journal of the Royal Astronomical Society* 18:1–32.

Marvin, U. B. 1973. *Continental Drift: The Evolution of a Concept.* Washington, D.C.: Smithsonian Institution Press.

Menard, H. W. 1969. The deep-ocean floor. *Scientific American* 221: 42–44, 126–132.

Suess, E. 1904–1924. *The Face of the Earth* [Das Antlitz der Erde]. Translated by H. B. C. Sollas. Oxford, England: Clarendon Press.

Wegener, A. 1924. *The Origins of Continents and Oceans.* Translated from the 3rd (1922) German edition of J. G. A. Skerl. London: Methuen.

Ophiolites

Gass, I. 1983. Ophiolites. *Scientific American* 247(2):122–131.

Lapham, D. M. 1978. The tectonic history of multiply deformed serpentinite in the Piedmont of Pennsylvania. In *Ultramafic and Related Rocks,* edited by P. J. Wyllie. New York: Interscience Publishing.

Steinmann, G. 1927. Die ophiolithischen Zonen in dem mediterranen Kettenbirge. *Fourteenth International Congress, Madrid* 2:638–667.

Freestone and Footwarmers

Chidester, A. H., A. L. Albee, and W. M. Cady. 1978. Petrology, structure, and genesis of the asbestos-bearing ultramafic rocks of the Belvidere Mountain area in Vermont. *United States Geological Survey Professional Paper* 1016.

Hess, H. H. 1955. Serpentine, orogeny, and epeiorogeny. *Geological Society of America Special Paper* 62:391–408.

———. 1962. In *Petrologic Studies: A Volume to Honor A. F. Buddington.* Boulder, Colorado: Geological Society of America.

Hitchcock, Edward et al. 1861. *Report on the Geology of Vermont—Descriptive, Theoretical, Economical, and Scenographical.* 2 volumes. Claremont, N.H.: Claremont Manufacturing.

Wyllie, P. J., ed. *Ultramafic and Related Rocks.* New York: Wiley.

Funeral Dress of Kings

Ballard, S. J. 1905. A second station for *Arenaria macrophylla. Rhodora* 7:156.

Brodeur, P. 1985. *Outrageous Misconduct: The Asbestos Industry on Trial.* New York: Pantheon.

Cady, W. M., A. L. Albee, and A. H. Chidester. 1963. Bedrock geology and asbestos deposits of the Upper Missisquoi Valley and vicinity, Vermont. *United States Geological Survey Bulletin* 1122-B.

Cody, W. J. 1983. *Adiantum pedatum* ssp. *calderi,* a new subspecies in northeastern North America. *Rhodora* 85:93–96.

Day, G. M. 1981. Abenaki place names in the Champlain Valley. *Int'l. Journal of American Linguistics* 47:143–171.

Engle, E. B. 1969. Old Ned of Eden Mills: a Vermont profile. *Vermont History* 37:265–271.

Fernald, M. L. 1900. *Rubus idaeus* and its variety *anomalous* in America. *Rhodora* 2:195–201.

Jolley, L. F. 1922. A variety of maidenhair fern new to Vermont. *Vermont Botanical and Bird Club Bulletin* 8:40–41.

Kruckeberg, A. R. 1952. Intraspecific variability in the response of certain native plant species in serpentine soils. *American Journal of Botany* 38:408–418.

———. 1967. Ecotypic response to ultramafic soils by some plant species of the northwestern United States. *Brittonia* 19:133–151.

Paris, C. 1986. A Biosystematic Investigation of the *Adiantum pedatum* complex in eastern North America. Unpublished master's thesis, Botany Department, University of Vermont.

Pringle, C. G. 1897. Reminiscences of botanical rambles in Vermont. *Burlington Free Press*, February 9, 1897.

Stebbins, G. L. 1942. The genetic approach to problems of rare and endemic species. *Madroño* 6:241–272.

Zika, P. F. and K. T. Dann. 1985. Rare plants on ultramafic soils in Vermont. *Rhodora* 87:293–304.

Mont Albert and the Nunatak Debate

Drury, W. H. 1969. Plant persistence in the Gulf of Saint Lawrence in K. N. H. Greenidge. *Symposium in Terrestrial Plant Ecology: Essays in Plant Geography and Ecology.* Halifax: Nova Scotia Museum.

Fernald, M. L. 1905. An alpine *Adiantum. Rhodora* 7:190–192.

———. 1907. Soil preferences of certain alpine and sub-alpine plants. *Rhodora* 9:149–193.

———. 1918. The geographical affinities of the vascular floras of New England, the maritime provinces and Newfoundland. *American Journal of Botany* 5:219–236.

———. 1924. Isolation and endemism in northeastern North America and their relation to the age-and-area hypothesis. *American Journal of Botany* 11:558–572.

———. 1925. The persistence of plants in unglaciated areas of boreal America. *Memoirs of the American Academy of Science* 15(3):239–342.

———. 1926–1927. Two summers of botanizing in Newfoundland. *Rhodora* 28:49–63, 74–87, 89–111, 115–129, 145–155, 161–178, 181–204, 210–225, 234–241.

————. 1942. Incidents of field-work with J. Franklin Collins. *Rhodora* 44:98–135.

————. 1950. *Gray's Manual of Botany.* 8th edition. New York: American Book.

Grant, D. R. 1977. Glacial style and ice limits, the Quaternary stratigraphic record, and changes of land and ocean level in the Atlantic Provinces, Canada. *Géographique physique quaternaire* 31:247–260.

Kucyniak, J. 1946. Frère Marie-Victorin. *Rhodora* 48:265–272.

Low, A. P. 1884. Report on explorations and surveys in the interior of Gaspé Peninsula, 1883. *Geological and Natural History Survey of Canada Report.*

Marie-Victorin, Frère. 1938. Phytogeographical problems in eastern Canada. *American Midland Naturalist* 19:498–558.

————. Unpublished diaries and correspondence of Frère Marie-Victorin, Jardin Botanique de Montréal, Montreal, Canada.

Rune, O. 1954. Notes on the flora of the Gaspé Peninsula. *Svensk. Botan. Tidsk.* 48:117–136.

Scoggan, H. J. 1950. The flora of Bic and the Gaspé Peninsula, Quebec. *Bulletin of the National Museum of Canada* 115.

Willis, J. C. 1922. *Age and Area: A Study in Geographical Distribution and Origin of Species.* Cambridge: Cambridge University Press.

Wynne-Edwards, V. C. 1937. Isolated arctic-alpine floras in eastern North America: a discussion of their glacial and recent history. *Transactions of the Royal Society of Canada* 3(31):1–26.

The Caledonian Connection

Allen, R. O., A. H. Luckenbach, and C. G. Holland. 1975. Application of instrumental neutron activation analysis to a study of prehistoric steatite artifacts and source materials. *Archaeometry* 17(1):69–83.

Allen, R. O., K. K. Allen, and W. W. Fitzhugh. 1978. Utilization of soapstone in Labrador by Indians, Eskimo, and Norse. *Nature* 271:237–239.

Allen, R. O., H. Hamroush, C. Nagle, and W. W. Fitzhugh. 1984. Use of rare earth element analysis to study the utilization and procurement of soapstone along the Labrador coast. *Archaeological Chemistry* 3:1–18.

Cumming, L. M. 1975. Geology of the L'Anse aux Meadows National Historical Park, northern Newfoundland. *Geological Survey of Canada Paper* 75-1, Part A.

Graham-Campbell, J. 1980. *The Viking World.* New Haven: Ticknor and Fields.

Ingstad, A. S. 1977. *The Discovery of a Norse Settlement in North America: Excavations at L'Anse aux Meadows, Newfoundland, 1961–1968.* Oslo: Universitetsforlaget.

Ingstad, H. 1969. *Westward to Vinland: The Discovery of Pre–Columbian Norse House-sites in North America.* London: Jonathan Cape.

Jones, G. 1961. *Erik the Red and Other Icelandic Sagas.* New York: Oxford University Press.

Munn, W. A. 1929. *Wineland Voyages: Location of Helluland, Markland, and Vinland.* St. Johns, Newfoundland: St. Johns Press.

Williams, H. 1978. Geological development of the northern Appalachians: its bearing on the evolution of the British Isles. In Crustal evolution in northwestern Britain and adjacent regions, edited by D. R. Bowes and B. E. Leake. *Geology Journal Special Issue* 10:1–22.

———. 1980. *Tectonic Lithofacies Map of the Appalachian Orogen.* St. Johns: Memorial University of Newfoundland.

Williams, H., and Pierre St.-Julien. 1982. The Baie Verte-Brompton line: early Paleozoic continent-ocean interface in the Canadian Appalachians. In Major structural zones and faults of the northern Appalachians, edited by P. St.-Julien and J. Béland. *Geological Association of Canada Special Paper* 24.

Wilson, D. M. 1980. *The Northern World: The History and Heritage of Northern Europe: A.D. 400–1100.* New York: Harry N. Abrams.

Index